About This Book

This book is an introduction to the colorful, fascinating world of wild flowers, a world of simple delights in a complex day and age. It is based on the idea that if a person knows the wild flowers, he will like them; if he likes them, he will have enjoyment of them and try to protect them— for they need protection, too.

You can use this book as a general guide to the four hundred flowers that you are most apt to come across.

But its wider purpose is to help you *know* the ways and whys of all wild flowers: It does not ask you to match a flower you do not know with a picture or a technical key in order to learn merely its name. It introduces you to the more complex but complete handbooks and field guides, one of which you might want to use as your knowledge of wild flowers increases. It stresses main features of groups of flowers, rather than a system based on color of blossom or section of the country or botanical detail.

Alfred Stefferud, the author, is the editor of the *Yearbook of Agriculture* of the United States Department of Agriculture. In that job each year he edits and writes something like 600,000 words of manuscript about trees, grasses, conservation, animals, insects, and many another scientific subject. On weekends he rides hobbies like flowers, nature study, and farming. He is a member of the Wild Flower Preservation Society and conducts a wide correspondence with fellow lovers of wild flowers all over the country. As teacher, reporter, foreign correspondent, and magazine writer and editor in earlier years, he has learned about flora and fauna in many parts of the world.

Sidney H. Horn, the illustrator, formerly was a member of the staff of Iowa State College. He is now a free-lance artist and specializes in scientific illustration. He has prepared drawings for many publications on natural history. His drawings for this book were made in outline to allow you to color them yourself. A color chart and guide is provided on the back cover.

How to Know the
WILD FLOWERS

by
ALFRED STEFFERUD

Illustrations by
SIDNEY H. HORN

Endorsed by the
Wild Flower Preservation Society

A MENTOR BOOK
Published by THE NEW AMERICAN LIBRARY

HOW TO KNOW THE WILD FLOWERS
is a joint publication of Henry Holt and Company, Inc., and The New American Library of World Literature, Inc.

FIRST PRINTING, MARCH, 1950

To

CHRISTINE'S MOTHER

MENTOR BOOKS are published by The New American Library of World Literature, Inc. 245 Fifth Avenue, New York 16, New York

PRINTED IN THE UNITED STATES OF AMERICA

CONTENTS

WE START AN ADVENTURE

This book began one Sunday afternoon when my young daughter Christine and I were hiking on Short Hill just behind our house.

It was a springtime rediscovery of things we had missed in winter—the rabbits busy in the bushes, squirrels talking in the trees, Dogwoods trying out their first leaves.

In a damp spot near a runnel we delightedly sniffed the rare smell of Skunk-Cabbage. Farther on we spied Bloodroots, their flowers still clasped in cylinders of leaves. We greeted drifts of Trilliums and Violets as old friends.

But now and then we came across a plant we did not know. One intrigued us because it grew in a clump of ferns, where we thought it should not be. One had leaves like an Oak, only larger. Another was definitely a Violet— but which one? We were disturbed, because this close to home we had found strangers.

I went on looking at trees, which were my particular interest. Christine resumed collecting moss and stones, which were hers. She was humming a verse we had sung that morning in Sunday School, "All nature sings, and round me rings, the music of the spheres."

She stopped: "Wouldn't it be fun to know the plants that grow in our own back yard and everything about them?"

"Everything?" I repeated. "Why, everything even here would take a thousand lifetimes with ecology, taxonomy, paleobotany—"

"Now, Dad," she scoffed. "You're trying to show off. I don't know a word you're saying. I don't care about that. I'd just like to know the names of flowers and who they are."

"Who?"

"Yes, the same as people. Where they live. What they are. Their families. What they are good for—"

"And why there are so many? Why some are red and others white? But couldn't you enjoy the flowers as much

7

just seeing them here? What difference if you call a Trillium a Trillium or Wake Robin or any name you make up, like 'White Lady'?"

"Well, maybe." She thought a moment. "But I wouldn't feel then that I really did know them."

"Hm. Very interesting," I said. Always a teacher because once a teacher, I continued: "I feel the same. What say we find out a detail or two about every group of wild flowers—enough so we can tell them apart and they become personalities to us?"

Chris liked the idea, and we started at once. How we began is told in the next chapter. In the months that followed we derived great enjoyment from collecting names and facts in our heads and notebooks. We did not collect the flowers themselves; we preferred to let them live. When (often enough) we encountered something we did not know, we consulted a field guide or reference book—which we found to be most enjoyable and useful but sometimes too complex and cryptic in wording. Now and then I got help and inspiration from Dr. P. L. Ricker, who is president of the Wild Flower Preservation Society and wise in the ways of nature.

Chris and I discovered, as we went along, that our adventure with wild flowers was giving us a deeper appreciation for every-day things—why bees visit some plants and not others, for example, and why flowers open at different times of the day and year.

We added to our store of knowledge, which I think is always a good thing, no matter what the knowledge. We unlocked a treasury of words. We got new insight into the orderliness of nature and of men who work with nature. Our wonder grew at the devices of plants for continuing their species. We had a glimpse of several sciences that closely touch our lives.

We came to feel ourselves part of a vital conservation movement, so important that I call it patriotism-in-action. Most of all, we had fun and relaxation, Christine from her sixth-grade books and I from other books that easily can be substitutes for living and finding out for one's self. All this from a simple subject, a pleasant adventure just outside our door!

Chris and I invite you to share that adventure with us.

8

THE FIRST STEP

Our first step was to learn the parts of a flower—the words that we use when we want to describe a plant.

So Christine and I sat down beside a Trillium in order to study it carefully. We did not pick the flower, lest we destroy the whole plant. Nor did we uproot it, because the root is seldom a key feature.

We began with the flower, as I suppose Nature intended when she created these jewels of many colors, many forms. Item by item (as shown on the next page) we identified:

The *calyx* (pronounced *kay*-licks), the outermost or the lowest set of floral parts. In many plants the calyx, which usually is green, is divided into segments called *sepals* (*see*-pulls). The calyx protects the organs within.

The *corolla* (kor-*oll*-uh) is the inner flower-cup. Its parts are called *petals*. Usually the petals are brightly colored or glistening white—the better to attract us to their beauty. As a result, insects are attracted to their pollen; seeds are formed and the species perpetuated.

Calyx and corolla together form the *perianth* (*pair*-ee-anth) and are regarded as accessory organs. That is, they are not absolutely essential for seed production, which is the main function of the flower. A flower that has both calyx and corolla we call a complete flower. One that lacks either calyx or corolla is incomplete.

The *stamens* (*stay*-mens) are the male organs. Sometimes they are called a long name that means "male household." Nearly always the stamen consists of a filament or stalk, which has at its apex the pollen sac, or anther. The anther liberates the pollen grains, the male reproductive elements.

The *pistil*, the innermost set of floral organs, is the "female household," the seed-bearing organ. Usually the individual pistil consists of the *stigma*, which has a moist or roughened surface and receives the male pollen; the *style*, which is the tube that leads to the ovary; and the ovary itself. The *ovary* is at the base of the pistil and contains the ovules, or eggs, which ripen into seeds or

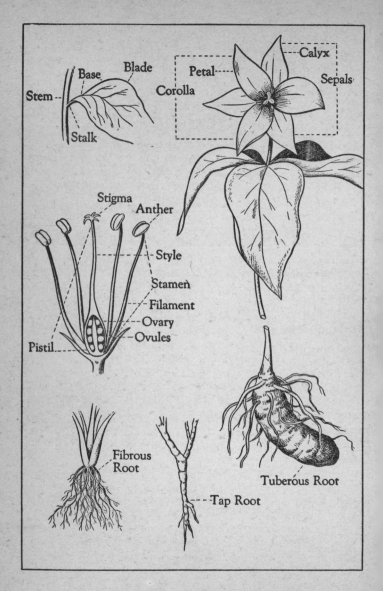

Here is a picture "dictionary" of many of the terms you will want to know about the flowers, leaves, and roots.

fruits after they are quickened into life by the pollen. As with animals, and as we shall see later, Nature uses many interesting devices to bring male and female elements together so that life can go on. The stamens and pistils (or carpels, as they are called sometimes) are the "essential" organs, because seed cannot be produced without them. Most plants have both sets of essential organs in their flowers and hence are said to be perfect. Imperfect flowers lack one set or the other.

The arrangement of the stamens and the position of the ovary are important in the identification of plants.

Next we examined the leaves of the Trillium. Leaves make food for the plant, give off excess water, and are the respiratory organs. Usually a leaf has three parts:

The *blade* is the widest part. When the blade is in one piece (as in the Trillium), it is a simple leaf. When it is divided into segments, or leaflets, it is compound.

The *stalk* (or *petiole*—pronounced *pet*-ee-ohl) supports the blade. If it is lacking, the leaf is sessile (*sess*-il).

The leaf base attaches the leaf to the stem. Sometimes, as in the Rose, we find small, leaflike organs at the leaf base. They are the *stipules* (*stipp*-yuhls).

The *stem* is the part that holds up the leaves so they can get the light the plant uses to manufacture food. It also carries materials from the root to the leaves and from leaves to roots. Sometimes the stem stores food. Some stems develop underground and often are mistaken for roots. The Potato is a stem (tuber), thickened for storage purposes. Other examples of underground stems are the corm (as in the Jack-in-the-Pulpit) and the bulb (as in the Lily).

Common types of *roots* are fibrous roots, which have many fine rootlets, like hairs; tap roots, which have one main body that tapers downwards, like that of a Carrot; and tuberous roots, thick and fleshy, as in the Dahlia.

Of course in spring we did not see the Trillium berry. The fascinating subject of seeds and fruits was to come later. But we learned a lot that first day.

"I never thought my eyes could see so much," said Chris.

"There is nothing in which people differ more than in their powers of observation," I said.

WHAT TO LOOK FOR

As we discovered later when we dissected the Violet and other flowers in the same way that we had cross-examined the Trillium, wild flowers of one species can differ from those of other species in one or several key features. These we made into a check-list of "leading questions" on what to look for.

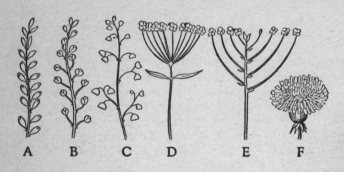

How are the flowers arranged?

Some flowers (like the Trillium and Violet) are borne singly, but many are clustered in one of the following:

a spike—attached directly along a single stem (like the Plantain—*A* in the drawing above).

a raceme (B)—similar to a spike, but each flower has a distinct stalk that attaches it to the flowering stem (examples: Larkspur, Lily of the Valley).

a panicle (C)—a compound raceme, in which flowers are arranged along the plant stem, but each flower stem has two or more branches (Meadow Buttercup, Phlox, Spanish Bayonet).

an umbel (D)—a cluster in which the pedicels rise from the same level (Milkweed).

a corymb (E)—a nearly flat-topped cluster (Yarrow).

a head (F)—many stalkless flowers bunched compactly, often with an outside row of specialized flowers or florets (Dandelion, Aster, Daisy, Thistle).

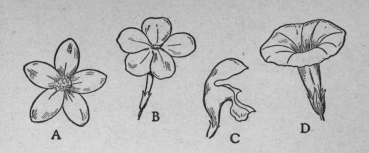

A   B   C   D

How is the perianth arranged?

Some of the simpler flowers, like the Cat-tail, have no perianth (petals and sepals) . In some, like the Sweet Flag, only a few scales compose the perianth.

In the higher plants, like the Lily, the perianth is a conspicuous part of the flower. Finally, among the Roses the sepals and petals are clearly distinct.

In the simpler flowers, sepals, petals, and stamens arise at the top of the flower cup. (A in the drawing above) .

The corolla (the petals) is regular when the petals have the same size and shape, as in Wild Rose, Phlox, and Poppy. (B)

The corolla is irregular when the petals have various shapes and sizes, as in the Orchid and Snapdragon. (C)

In some flowers (Buttercup, Geranium) the petals are free from each other. In some (Foxglove, Morning Glory) the petals are fused for all or part of the corolla. (D)

Sometimes we can identify a whole group of flowers by the form or shape of the corolla. For example, members of the Mustard family have four spreading petals (like D, in the drawing on page 15) . The Mints have a somewhat two-lipped corolla (C, above) . A mark of the Legume group is the "butterfly" form—or "papilionaceous" as the botanists say—in which there are two wing petals, an upper petal or banner, and two lower petals often somewhat united to form a keel.

And why should one know these details? Simply because if one knows the general plan of flowers, whether Morning Glory or Pea or any other, he will soon know the specific plan of one flower and then of many flowers.

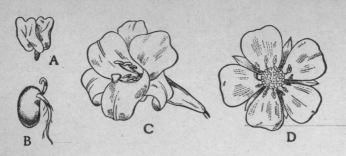

How many parts does the flower have?

In the evolution of flowers from the more primitive forms to higher forms, the number of organs, the ways in which they are joined, and their symmetry have changed. On bases such as those we can arrange the 195,000 species of flowering plants in this world into groupings which show common characteristics and which, therefore, help us to tell one from another. Thus, a species (the smallest grouping with which we need be concerned) is a group of plants that are alike in all important respects but are different from all others. A genus is a grouping of related species. Genera (the plural of genus) of like plants are put into families, families are grouped into orders, orders into subclasses, and subclasses into classes.

There are two main classes of flowering plants. The Monocotyledons (or Monocots, for short) have one cotyledon or seed-leaf to their embryo and usually their flower parts are based on the number three—three sepals, three petals, three stamens. Among the Monocots are the Arrow Head, Trillium, Day Flower, Arum, Lily, Onion, Iris, Orchid. (B and C in the drawing above.)

The other main class is the Dicotyledons (or Dicots), which have a pair of cotyledons, or seed leaves (A and D in the drawing). Their floral symmetry usually rests on the numbers four or five. Among them are the Water-Lily, Buttercup, Poppy, Geranium, Pink, Pea, Violet, Rose, Mint.

Although we commonly use only the genus and species names to identify a plant, it is well to see how the whole plant kingdom fits together before we look at one part of it.

What is Its shape?

The form of the corolla often helps us to recognize plants of certain genera. Or—still more important, perhaps—an examination of details like these will prove again to us how manifold and how wonderful are the works of God and Nature.

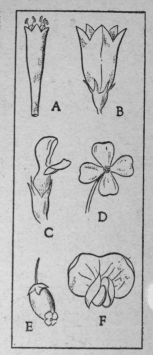

A (in the drawing opposite) is the trumpet shape (Honeysuckle).

B: Bell (Harebell).

C: Two-lipped (Sage, Nettle). One of the irregular forms, and quite common.

D: Cross-shaped (Mustards).

E: Barrel-shaped.

F: Butterfly-shaped (Pea).

What is Its color?

Very likely those of us who are not full-fledged botanists are more aware of color than any other characteristic of a flower. Indeed, several good wild flower guides are organized according to color. But I think one should not rely too much on that, for color can vary even in flowers of the same genus because of amount of shade, sun, season, and other factors. Also color (or the sense of color) is in one's own eye—who can define lavender and lilac and violet precisely? A color chart and guide might help you— but the purpose of our study of wild flowers will be defeated if we do no more than to try to match some color with a name that seems to fit it.

What is the general shape of the leaf?

In the drawing at top of page 16, A is ribbon-shaped; B is lance-shaped; C is oblong; D is oval; E is heart-

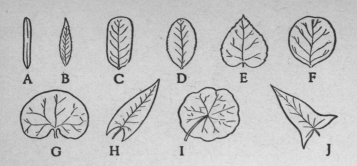

shaped; F is rounded; G is kidney-shaped; H is arrow-shaped; I is shield-shaped; and J is halberd-shaped. Note that these shapes are all of a piece, so to speak.

But sometimes leaves are cut up, divided, lobed, or cleft into parts or lobes or divisions, as in the drawing below.

A and F are lobed leaves; the parts of segments are rounded, and the cuts are blunt.

B and G are cleft—they are cut about half-way, and the cuts are sharp and narrow.

C and D are parted; they are cut almost clear through to the base of the leaf.

E is divided; its divisions go through to the base.

A, B, and C are *pinnate,* or veined like a feather. That is, their main veins spring from the midrib.

F, G, D, and E are *palmate* (like the palm of a hand). The veins run toward the base of the blade.

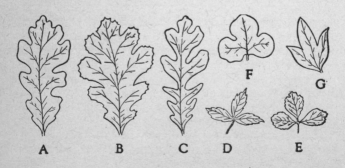

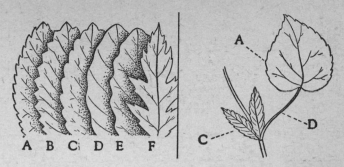

In the drawing above, left, A is saw-toothed, or *serrate;* B is *dentate* (the teeth point outward) ; C is scalloped or *crenate;* D is *wavy;* E is strongly wavy or *sinuate;* F is *incised* or jagged.

Above, to the right, are the parts of a leaf. A is the blade; sometimes it is narrow, like a needle. D is the *petiole,* the stalk that supports the blade. C is the *stipules,* small organs like leaves.

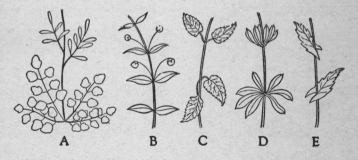

Some other terms that describe leaves are shown above:

A: A *compound* leaf (divided into *leaflets*) . The upper ones are *alternate;* only one grows at a node and each is opposite and above the preceding leaf.

B: The *simple* leaves (of one piece only) are *opposite* (in pairs opposite each other on the same node) . From the place where the leaves join the stem, the axils, arise flowers, which are called *axillary.*

C: The leaves are opposite and lance-shaped.

D: The leaves, on the same joint, form a circle, or *whorl.* E: The leaves almost *clasp* the stem.

17

WE LOOK AT SOME FLOWERS

To sharpen your eyes and make you more aware of Nature's devices and purposes (which is better than relying on a book) you will want to ask yourself other questions.

How tall is the plant? (How is it equipped to compete with other plants for sunlight?)

Where does it grow—roadside, bog, dense forest, open thicket, pasture? (You will learn why not to look for the Moccasin Flower on a hot, sandy railroad embankment.)

When does it blossom? (Item: You would not find a Trillium among Goldenrods. Item: Early bloomers tend to have food-filled, thick rootstocks, ready for an early spring growth.)

Which insects visit it? (Hummingbirds like red flowers. Bees like blue ones. Moths like white, fragrant, night-blooming flowers. Those that depend on the wind, not insects, for pollination, do not have gay flowers.)

Does the plant have hairy or downy leaves, stems, or flowers? (The hairs allow certain insects to visit and pollinate the flower but repel others.)

What kind of fruit does it have? This could be the subject of a whole book. Fruits—containing the seeds—are the matured pistils of the flower, and its objective in life. They may be edible or not, fleshy or dry. A berry is a fleshy fruit—like cranberries and grapes. An akene is dry, one-seeded, closed, and small. Like it, but larger, is a nut. Pods, when dry and ripe, generally split lengthwise. A capsule is the pod of any compound pistil.

Does it have any strange habits?—such as closing on cloudy days, blossoming only at dusk, drooping when you touch it, or maturing stamens before the pistils?

No need to know all the answers—at first. Christine and I found (as you will, too) that we absorbed such information more easily as we learned to look more and more appreciatively at the main features of *groups* of flowers, instead of going through the thousands of species in this country, one by one.

And now, with that in mind and the joy of adventure in our hearts, let us look at some wild flowers.

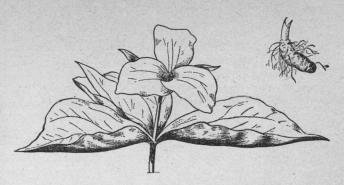

THE TRILLIUMS

We have already been introduced to the Trillium. It merits further acquaintance: It is one of the first flowers in spring. It is bold and brilliant. It is worth planting in your own wild garden.

Its 30-odd species grow west to the Plains and Northwest. They have tuberous underground stems. Usually they are up to 18 inches high. You can identify a Trillium easily if you remember that its parts are in threes—three broad leaves (its name derives from *tri-folium,* three-leaved), three green sepals, three petals, three carpels, three times two stamens.

The Great Trillium, illustrated above, is the best known species. Its single, showy white flower, above the dark-green and droopy leaves and on a stalk up to three inches long, fades to pink as it ages. It grows in woods.

The Toad Trillium has brown or greenish-brown petals. Its leaves have brown spots.

The Nodding Trillium has a white or pinkish flower on a short stalk that hangs downward. The rather narrow petals curve outward. It blossoms about ten days later than the white or red Trilliums and it likes swamps and rich, moist woods. Stemless Trillium has purplish flowers.

The Red Trillium has a stout stem, dark green leaves, and a large flower. Large-leaf is similar.

The Painted Trillium carries its flower, whose white petals have a pink or crimson patch at the base, on a nearly erect stalk. It needs moist, acid soil, and is harder than the others to cultivate.

THE ARROW HEADS

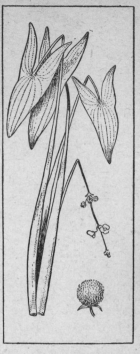

You meet the Arrow Heads in summer in wet places the country over. The delicate white flowers grow in whorls of three on thick stalks. They have three green sepals, three petals, and many stamens and carpels. The male flowers are in separate clusters above the female flowers and, being more showy, are visited first by insects, which later carry the pollen to the females. Thus Nature insures that even this primitive plant gets pollen.

Look closely at the leaves and you will see another phenomenon of Nature. The leaves above the water are several inches wide and (as you would guess from the name) shaped like an arrow head. But if the plant grows in deep water which would damage a broad blade, the leaves are narrow, like grass, and offer less resistance to the current.

Broadleaf Arrow Head is the most common of our many kinds of Arrow Heads. Early Indians ate their starchy tubers. It is easily cultivated—maybe too easily to have in small pools. It usually grows about two feet high, but sometimes is only a few inches tall. Its common name is a translation of the Latin: *Sagittaria* (arrow) and *latifolia* (broadleaved). The leaves grow directly from the root. It blossoms in August and September.

Lanceleaf Arrow Head sometimes grows six feet high.

Water Plantain, a close relative of the Arrow Head, averages two feet in height and has many tiny, white, three-petalled flowers. The leaves are pointed and egg-shaped, and are borne on long stalks. It lives in wet places or shallow water almost everywhere.

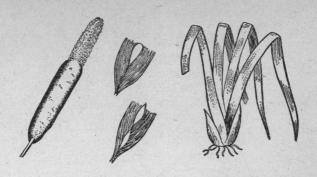

THE CAT-TAILS

The Cat-tails hold little interest for the botanist. They are a small family of one genus and three species. But for children and those of us who recall a country childhood they hold pleasure beyond price.

We made mats of their erect, grasslike leaves. We hid in their thick clumps along river banks or ditches until the "Indians" were safely past. We gathered the fluffy hairs of the fruit for pillows and dipped the flower spikes in kerosene for torches. We ate the cooked underground rootstalks and the tender shoots. Our mothers kept the flower stems, three or six feet tall, as parlor bouquets that lasted all winter. Simple joys, those, of simple days.

We did not know, though, that the Cat-tail spike actually may contain several thousand flowers tightly packed together. The top part of the spike bears the male flowers. It is yellowish and thinner than the plump, brown portion below, which bears the female flower. The wind can carry the ripe fruits many miles because of their silky hairs. Indians used the fluff of the seeds for wrapping papooses. So important was the Cat-tail to them that they sometimes went to war for possession of marshes where Cat-tails grew.

The Broad-leaf Cat-tail (above) grows in marshes throughout this country.

The Narrow-leaf Cat-tail is much like it. It is more abundant in coastal marshes and has narrower leaves, which are one-sixth to one-half inch wide. The spikes are a lighter brown and not so thick.

DAY FLOWERS

The dainty blue Day Flowers got their names from two characteristics. The flowers open one or two at a time and wither in a day or less—hence Day Flower. Two of the three petals are showy; the third is insignificant—hence the family and species name Commelina, after the three Dutch brothers Commelin, two of whom were eminent scientists. The third was an ordinary citizen.

All Day Flowers have leafy stems. The three sepals are green or bronzy. Stamens number six and carpels three.

The Tall Day Flower is rather coarse and two or three feet high. It puts forth its bilateral flowers all summer in a cluster that arises from partly united bracts (brackets). A bract is a modified leaf surrounding certain flowers. The leaves are lance-shaped. It grows from southern New York south to Florida and west to Kansas and Texas.

The Low Day Flower is more delicate. Its branching stems root at the nodes. The flowers are strongly bilateral or butterfly-like. The sepals are bronzy. It grows in the south of Delaware and west to Texas in open woods and thickets.

The Asiatic Day Flower, named for its origin, is widely naturalized south of New York. In summer and fall it grows sprawlingly on moist banks and waste ground. Its third petal is white and small.

Another of our species is the Baby Dewflower, which likes sandy places, stream banks, and fields from Indiana to Florida and Texas.

Related to Day Flowers are the Roselings, which are upright plants two inches to two feet tall. They have rush-like leaves, bunches of fuzzy roots, and clusters of pink or purple flowers, each of which has three showy petals.

Like their relatives the Spiderworts, the Day Flowers shrivel at noon into a jellyish mass—a device to keep a flower from being fertilized by its own pollen. Do not pick them; if you do, the petals quickly become pulpy or liquid. Hence they are sometimes called Job's Tears or Widow's Tears, but really there is nothing unhappy about them.

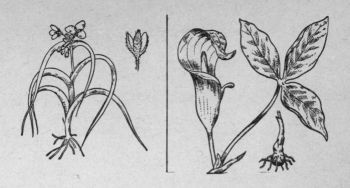

SPIDERWORTS

The Spiderworts have long, narrow, bright green leaves and handsome purplish-blue flowers in umbels. Below are one to three leaflike bracts. They blossom most of the summer.

Most frequent is the Spider-Lily, Common Spiderwort, Its pedicels—the stalk of a sperate flower in a cluster—and sepals are hairy, and the flowers are an inch or two broad. It is a friendly, adaptable flower, and one to be prized. It grows along streams, on hillsides, in rich woods, thickets, and stony bluffs from the Atlantic seaboard west to South Dakota and south to Texas. It may reach a height of three feet, depending on soil conditions.

Reflexed Spiderwort is much like it, except that its leaves are blue-green, its flower stalks are smooth, and it prefers more sandy places, dunes, barrens, and pinelands from Ohio to Kansas and Minnesota and south to South Carolina and Texas.

Long-bracted Spiderwort (illustrated above, left) can be identified by the white, broad, sac-like bases of the bracts, which emphasize the reddish-blue color of the petals.

Others of the dozen species are the Pineland Spiderwort, a beautiful flower that has tuberous roots, and the Texas Spiderwort, a four-to-twelve-inch dwarf that has bright blue or rosy flowers and hairy stems and calyxes. Spiderworts differ from Day Flowers in having petals all alike and—usually—six stamens, not three.

THE ARUMS

You can easily spot an Arum by three outstanding features: They grow in wet ground. The tiny flowers are grouped closely on a fleshy spike. The spike is like a thumb, and always wrapped in a leaf-like sheath. Of the twenty-one species of Arums, we know best the Jack-in-the-Pulpit, Golden Club, and Skunk-Cabbage. All are strange and fascinating.

Jack-in-the-Pulpit is a foot high, maybe two. It has one to three long-stalked leaves; each leaf is divided into three leaflets, rather large. The small flowers, without sepals or petals, grow near the base of the columnar spike, or thumb or spadix, which the uninitiated might call the flower itself. Around the spadix is a beautiful hood, a spathe, which arches over the flower cluster and forms the pulpit.

The several kinds of Jacks differ mainly in the striping of the green, purple, or white spathe.

Woodland Jack-in-the-Pulpit is brown striped. Its albino forms have green stripes. It is shown on page 23.

Swamp Jack is about a foot high and nearly black.

Northern Jack has white ridges outside and brown stripes inside.

The Jacks appear in spring or very early summer from the eastern seaboard west to Kansas and southward to Florida and Louisiana. The fruit is a cluster of bright red berries in the fall. They are sometimes called Indian Turnip because the Indians boiled and ate the bitter-tasting corm or used it, unboiled and acrid, to test the hardiness of young braves.

Golden Club has an unforgettable trademark—the tiny, golden-yellow flowers that tip a thick, round spike (or spadix, as we should call it), which rises above the surface of swamps, ponds and streams. Another feature is the bluish-green leaves, up to a foot long and two to five inches wide, which often are iridescent and float on the water. Its roots creep deep into the mud. You find it in early spring from Massachusetts to Florida and Louisiana. Some people name it Never-wet or Fireleaf because its leaves shed water.

24

Skunk-Cabbage there is no mistaking. In some places it is the earliest of all spring flowers; it comes before the snow is gone. Its inch-thick spadix is entirely covered with inconspicuous, perfect flowers, and is enclosed in a fleshy, thick hood (spathe, you remember) that is three to six inches long and purplish-brown, yellow, and purple in color. The spathe appears out of the ground before the large, spade-shaped leaves—often three feet long and a foot wide—appear from the thick stem base. Skunk-Cabbage grows in low, wet woods, meadows, and swamps from New England west to Minnesota and Iowa and south to North Carolina and Missouri. If you bruise any part of the plant, you will find out why it got its name.

Wild Calla is a showy swamp plant. At the top of its short flower stalk, about six inches long, is a knob of tiny greenish flowers that usually have no sepals or petals. Guarding the flowers, as in the other Arums, is a bract that is white inside and greenish outside. The shiny green leaves are heart-shaped. The rootstocks are long, creeping, and bitter to taste. It grows in cold, wet northern places.

Green Dragon has green flowers in a round cluster at the base of a narrow greenish or whitish axis, which extends like a tail five inches or so beyond the whitish tube that enwraps it. Its stalk, two or three feet high, bears a large leaf divided into five to seventeen leaflets. This interesting plant is less abundant than the Jack-in-the-Pulpit.

The Sweet Flag is common in wet meadows, swamps, and streams as far west as Kansas and south to Texas. Its leaves are long ribbons. The minute, greenish-yellow flowers cover a spike that is two or three inches long.

BUNCHFLOWERS

As you would expect from the name, the Bunchflowers (or Bunchlilies) have their tiny, pale-colored individual flowers massed in eye-catching bunches, sometimes as many as several thousand in a head. The flower parts (since this is a monocot) are in threes. Sepals and petals are much alike and become firm and persistent. The leaves are grass-like. The fruit is a capsule.

Turkey Beard is two or three feet high. In late spring the small white flowers make a dense cylinder. From a thick stem base grow many wiry leaves in a rosette. You find it in sandy pinelands and oak woods (in acid soil, that is) from New Jersey to Tennessee.

Elkgrass, slightly larger, flourishes on dry ridges in the West. A truly noble plant, its dry, rough leaves make a basal tuft up to six feet across. From it rises a single unbranched stem, two to six feet tall, at the top of which is a mass of hundreds of creamy white flowers. Indians used to make clothing of its leaf fibers and roasted and ate the rootstocks.

Bunchlily is about the same. It is rough, hairy, and three feet or so high. The flower head has many medium-sized flowers in hairy panicles about a foot long. Each flower is three-fourths inch broad and greenish-yellow or brown, when it ages. The ribbon-like leaves are often a foot long and less than an inch wide. The lower leaves sheath the stem; the upper leaves are smaller and sessile.

It is found in July and August in meadows, wet woods, and marshes from Rhode Island inland to Minnesota and Texas. It is pictured on page 26.

Northern Camas is similar, but poisonous. On a stalk a foot or two high are a few medium-sized flowers with broad sepals and petals, greenish white with a green disk at the base. The leaves are gray-green and arise from a bulb. It grows among grasses and bushes in limy meadows and damp pockets in limestone rocks through the north.

White Hellebore, or Indianpoke, stands three to five feet high. Its medium-sized flowers, in compound heads, are yellowish-green in petals and sepals. The leaves are short, broad, veiny, and alternate in three rows up the stalk. The thick underground stem is used as an insecticide.

Fairy Wand has a wand-like stalk, two or three feet tall, on which are small white flowers in early summer. It grows in damp, open woods in the South and Northeast. The leaves are like those of lilies and form rosettes from the thick underground stems.

Swamp Hyacinth has a hollow stalk that is only a few inches high when the dense flower heads start to open. Sepals and petals are a dull pink at first, but become more green when the stalk lengthens. Stamens are lavender. It blooms in spring in swamps and bog margins.

Viscid Triantha, for all its names, is an attractive plant. Known also as Glutinous Triantha, False Asphodel, and Tofieldia glutinosa, it is not common, but wild flower fans like to seek out this rare plant in peaty bogs from Minnesota to the Alleghenies. The greenish white flowers are grouped in threes in a short bunch. The short stalk bears dark glands.

Bog Asphodel has a dense bunch of medium-sized flowers that have yellow sepals and petals and hairy stamens. Its small, grass-like leaves are set edge to edge. It inhabits lowlands from New Jersey to Carolina.

Pickerel-weed, one of a small group of water plants, has white or blue flowers in a showy, four-inch spike. Each flower bears a greenish spot. Leaves are stout and arrow-shaped. It occurs widely through the East. The plant is up to three feet high.

THE LILIES

The simple facts tell less than the whole truth about the two thousand kinds of Lilies. They grow from underground bulbs. Their narrow leaves are usually in whorls —a main feature of Lilies. Sepals, petals, and carpels are in threes; stamens are two times three. The shape of the flowers is regular but distinctive—a tube whose segments flare outward. The petals have a firm texture. The flowers often are sweetly fragrant.

The whole truth, rather, is in your own mind and eye: Their brilliance, adaptability to so many conditions, susceptibility to cultivation and hybridizing are for you to experience yourself. Consider also Jesus' words that Solomon himself was not arrayed like one of these.

Turkscap Lily is outstanding in this colorful parade. On an impressive stem up to ten feet tall are circles ("whorls") of three to eight smooth, glossy-green, willow-like leaves. Sepals and petals are orange, red, or orange-yellow. The purple-spotted petals are up to four inches long and curve back at the tips so as to disclose a green star. Each plant produces some forty nodding flowers in an open grouping. Each flower is alone. The anthers are more than a half inch long. The Turkscap grows from New England to Virginia and west to Minnesota and Arkansas in meadows and wet ground.

Do not confuse Turkscap *(Lilium superbum)* and Day-Lily *(Hermerocallis fulva)*. Day-Lily has six or more deep orange flowers on a stalk, and long, flat leaves that rise only from the base.

Michigan Lily differs from the Turkscap in having smaller anthers, smaller size, and one to ten flowers, which radiate from the same point. Petals and sepals curve back so their tips touch.

Wood Lily has erect (not nodding) flowers, one to five to a stem. The petals are four inches long, straight and orange-red, with purple spots at the base. It grows among grasses in dry places in humus-rich, acid soil from Canada to North Carolina.

Canada Lily (illustrated, page 28) grows straight up to several feet. The yellow flowers are yellow with brown spots, two or three inches long, and bell-shaped. They have six spreading points. The lance-shaped leaves grow six or seven in a whorl. It blooms in June and July from Quebec to Georgia, west to Minnesota and Missouri.

THE TROUT-LILIES

Look for a nodding, glistening bell of a flower on a stalk a few inches high between two mottled leaves—that is a Trout-Lily. Little matter if you call it Dog-tooth-Violet, Fawn-Lily, or Adder's Tongue (which are not very good names for this gem)—this is one of America's favorites. Its seventeen species, members of the Lily family and genus *Erythronium,* grow from corms that are deeply buried. The stems therefore are half below the surface.

Yellow Trout-Lily has solitary yellow flowers about two inches long, which sometimes are purple-tinged, spotted near the base, or bronzy on the outside. The anthers (which, you remember, carry the powdery male pollen) are red or yellow. The stem is six to twelve inches long. The two leaves are oblong, lance-shaped, flat, and dark, glossy green. It grows in open woods from New Brunswick to Georgia and west to Nebraska.

White Trout-Lily, much the same, has white flowers, blooms more freely, and grows farther west from Ontario to New Jersey and west to Minnesota and Texas.

Midland Trout-Lily has plain leaves and lavender or pale blue flowers. It likes the prairies and grassy slopes in Iowa, Oklahoma, Missouri, Nebraska, and Kansas.

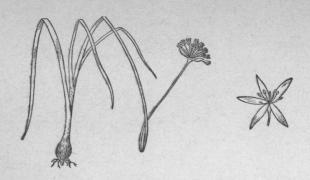

THE ONIONS

There's no mistaking the Onion family. The sap of many of the three hundred-odd species has a strong smell. The small flowers are in umbels, clusters in which the individual flowers arise from one point at the top of the stalk. The base of the stem is bulb-like, and the leaves look like those of grass or the Lilies. One, the Wild Garlic, has tubular leaves and is the bane of dairymen and home owners when it grows in pastures and lawns, but several others are pretty enough:

Summer Wild Onion, or Lady's Leek, puts forth nodding clusters of rose, lilac, or white flowers on a slender, foot-high, two ridged stalk. It appears in summer on sunny banks and slopes through most of the country.

Autumn Wild Onion has erect flowers, rosy-lilac, and prefers rocky banks and gravelly soils of the prairies.

Wood Leek, sometimes called Ramps or Rampscallions and used as food, has a leaf about a foot tall and an inch or two wide that withers before the white flower clusters come. It likes rich woods and damp places.

False Garlic is showy, odorless, narrow-leaved, and yellow-flowered, or white with yellow eyes. It is less than a foot high, and favors thickets and sandy spots.

Spring Wild Onion bears lavender flowers in late spring. It occurs in the Eastern states in open woods.

JOHN LOCKE: *Nature never makes excellent things for mean or no uses.*

THE CLINTONIAS AND BELLWORTS

The Clintonias are kin to the Solomon's Seal, Fairy Bells, Merrybells, and Bellworts. All belong to the Lily-of-the-Valley family and possess rather small, bell-shaped flowers, an underground main stem, and distinctive leaves. They resemble the lovely, fragrant cultivated Lily-of-the-Valley and the wild kind of the Blue Ridge and Appalachians.

Yellow Beadlily, or Northern Clintonia, brightens deep woods and swampy hummocks in the Northeast in early spring. Its yellow bells, three-fourths inch long, are attached loosely to an unbranched, eight-inch stalk that stands higher than the two or three, broad, thick, shiny leaves. Its dark blue berry is somewhat poisonous and looks like a bead or the end of a hatpin—hence its other names of Bluebead and Blue Beadlily.

White Beadlily has white petals and sepals. The eight-inch stalk carries many speckled flowers in a cluster. The three or four leaves form a rosette. The berry is a black bead. It is found in the mountains from New York to Georgia.

You can tell the Bellworts by their single or paired yellow bells that droop in a tired sort of way from a forked stem a foot or two high. They bloom in spring in light woods almost everywhere and are well worth having in one's own wild garden.

Great Bellwort has hairy leaves, the base of which encircles tightly the stem. Each fork of the round stalk carries a bright yellow, one-inch flower. Smooth Bellwort is like it, except its bells are paler in color, the gray-green leaves are smooth, and it prefers eastern woodlands.

Wildoats, or Strawlily, and the Haybell are related plants that differ in degree of hairiness.

GOETHE: *No one feels himself easy in a garden which does not look like the open country.*

SOLOMON'S SEALS

These plants get their name from the scars left on the creeping underground rootstock when the stem withers away from it. Some people think the scars look like seals made in wax. The flowers are small, greenish white, and hang down below the leaves, which grow erectly on the arching stems. The main difference between one or another of the eight species is size. Nearly all of them are big and tall and, with their lustrous leaves at the tops, are prepossessing indeed. They thrive in rich, shady places and are suitable for the wild garden.

King Solomon's Seal grows to five feet tall. From the axils of the smooth, alternate leaves arise clusters of two to eight nodding, three-fourths inch flowers. It is found in moist woods and fields from western New England south to Georgia and west to the Rocky Mountains. Its berries are blue-black pellets.

Hairy Solomon's Seal has a zigzag stalk two or three feet high. The leaves are four inches long and two inches wide, and are hairy on the underside. It inhabits dry woods from Maine to Minnesota, and south to Florida. Smooth Solomon's Seal is illustrated above.

Giant Solomon's Seal attains a height of eight feet or more. As many as fifteen flowers, each about three-fourths of an inch long, form a cluster. The leaves are a half-foot long and nearly as wide.

Northern Solomon's Seal prefers forests of maple and oak. Its flowers are green.

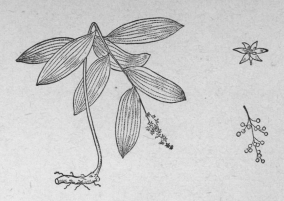

SOLOMON'S PLUMES

The Plumes of Solomon have tiny star-shaped flowers that grow in plume-like clusters at the tips of the stalks. You need not confuse them with the Solomon's Seals if you bear in mind that the Seals bear tubular flowers in the axils of the leaves. Solomon's Plumes (which also are called False Solomon's Seal) are of the genus *Smilacina;* Solomon's Seals, *Polygonatum.*

In late spring on wooded slopes in eastern and southern states appear the white flowers of Solomon's Plume, which has graceful, arching stalks two to three feet high. The showy panicles are six inches long and three inches broad. The stamens extend beyond the petals. The many leaves have hairy edges and prominent veins, and are up to six inches long and half as wide. A picture of it appears at the top of this page.

Starry Solomon's Plume has larger and fewer flowers, a shorter stalk (about twenty inches), and short stamens. The berries are green with black stripes. The five-inch leaves are downy underneath and often are folded lengthwise. It is not particular as to habitat.

Bog Solomon's Plume inhabits wet, cold bogs. It has few white flowers on a stalk less than a foot high.

It is easy to grow Solomon's Plume in moist places.

POPE: *All are but parts of one stupendous Whole, whose body Nature is, and God the soul.*

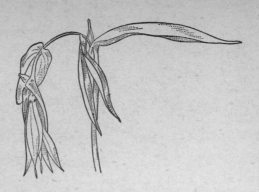

FAIRYBELLS

Greenish-white flowers, bell-shaped and nodding at the tips of leafy stalks, distinguish these inhabitants of northern wooded slopes. The plant is a foot or two tall. The leaves are downy and sessile. The fruit is a red berry. Its picture is printed above.

Spotted Fairybells are yellow with black dots. They grow in the South. Yellow Fairybells lack the dots.

Western Fairybells grows in the West. Its yellowish or white flowers yield scarlet, leathery fruit.

In the far west are found California Fairybells, whose bells are green, and Fairylantern, which is off-white. The last likes stream banks; the others prosper in forests in neutral to slightly acid soils.

Twisted-stalks

One is apt to call these by other names if one forgets their two main features: The flowers have flaring, recurved tips, and they grow in the leaf axils, not in tip clusters. As the name tells, the stalks are distinctly twisted or kinked in the middle.

Rosybells has rose-purple flowers and alternate leaves that have hairy margins. It favors swamps and cool woods in the Northeast. It is less than two feet tall.

Of wider range, between Greenland and New Mexico, is the greenish-white-flowered and smooth-leaved plant named Twisted-stalk, Pagoda Bells, or Liverberry.

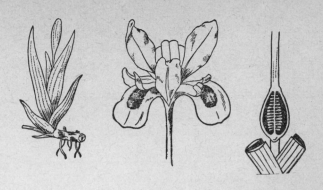

IRIS

Little description and no poetry is needed here for the Iris, however much of both has been applied to this rainbow flower since the age of fable. You know its main features: Sword-like, blue-green, firm leaves set edge-to-edge; thick rootstocks or rhizomes (underground stems from which roots grow) and bracted groups of flowers that are shortlived but of nearly every hue and unique form. It is a comparatively small family, but a sturdy and adaptable one, and few indeed are the localities without Iris.

Crested Iris (illustrated above) is a half foot high. The flowers vary from lavender-blue to white. The sepal has a yellow crest. It likes rocky or sandy slopes, lightly shaded from Maryland to Georgia and west to Oklahoma.

Blue Flag flaunts its lavender-blue crowns in May and June in wet meadows, thickets, marshes, and margins of ponds through the eastern half of North America. The bases of the sepals are bronzy-yellow, three or four inches across. The flower stalks are two-three feet high.

Great Blue Flag has broader leaves and down on the bases of the sepals. Its home is the Prairie States.

Copper Iris, a glowing red-bronze and two feet tall, is found along the Mississippi in wet places in late spring. Like other Iris, it has three each of petals and sepals.

Vernal Iris is a little gem only a few inches high. It has narrow leaves, blue flowers, and the scent of Violets. It needs poor, acid soil on sandy slopes. It is found in Middle Eastern States in early spring.

THE ORCHIDS

Orchids are for the millions, if one but knew it. From Arctic to Tropics grow 17,000 kinds; in the United States there are 300-odd species, varieties, and hybrids, not including those in florists' shops. So varied are they in habits, size, and looks that it is hard to find their common denominator.

Orchids have three sepals that are much alike. Of the three petals, however, the two lateral ones are similar, but the third is irregular and forms a strange structure called a lip, pouch, sac, or slipper. (The scientific name *Orchis* means testicle.) The lip or pouch is part of a wonderful mechanism to attract a particular insect—sometimes, even, one sex of one species of insect—and then to make sure the insect effects pollination.

All orchids are perennials—that is, they live more than one year; annual plants sprout, grow, blossom, bear seed, and die between spring and winter. Some orchids grow in soil; some are epiphytic—they get their living from the air. Leaves of Orchids generally are narrow, oblong, or rounded. The one or two stamens are fused with the style to form a column. The pollen is in waxy masses. The ovary is one-celled.

Orchid seeds are minute, almost like dust, and are difficult to germinate because they have no endosperm, the nutritious tissue that surrounds the seed embryo.

Orchids are the most highly specialized of the monocots, which, you recall, are one of the two main divisions of flowering plants and have a floral symmetry usually in threes.

Orchids are hard to cultivate; slugs and mice relish them; their tiny seeds are difficult to handle; at their roots they need special, highly cooperative fungi, called mycorrhiza, from which they get food. Therefore, do not pick any wild Orchids.

Botanists, understandably, do not agree on names of this diverse group of 450 genera, but here let us take a closer look at six types, the Lady's Slippers, Orchis, Rein-Orchids, Ladies' Tresses, Fringe-Orchids, and Coral-roots.

MOCCASINS AND SLIPPERS

The Moccasin Flowers have an opening in the lip for insects to enter, and their leaves grow from the ground line without stems. The Lady's Slippers differ from them in both respects, but here we can overlook such points and consider them all as of the genus *Cypripedium* (sip-ri-*peed*-ee-um). Furthermore, let us fix in our minds the main features of one of them, and a few words will suffice for the others, spectacular though they be.

The easiest to grow in one's own garden, and therefore worthy of special note, is the Yellow Lady's Slipper, which inhabits rich woods as far west as Colorado and south to Alabama. It is illustrated above. Its leafy stems are up to thirty inches high; the downy leaves are oval and pointed, up to six inches long and three inches wide. The flowers come in early summer singly or in pairs. They are one to three inches long and are yellow or golden. The inflated lip is yellow. The two sepals and spiraled petals are bronzy; they have purple stripes, which guide insects to the nectar within.

Showy Lady's Slipper is larger and maybe even more beautiful: The stout stem is leafy to the top and up to three feet high. The leaves are eight inches or so long and half that wide. The flowers, sometimes three together, are white with white and crimson stripes. The greatly inflated lip is often two inches long.

It grows in swamps and rich, moist grasslands from Newfoundland south to Georgia and west to Minnesota.

37

Pink Moccasin Flower: A solitary flower two inches long; the lip is pink with red veins. It prefers rich bogs and woods, strongly acid.

Small White Lady's Slipper: Twelve inches tall, or less; its white lip is purple-striped inside.

Golden Slipper: One to three bronzy, fragrant flowers in a row, with a yellow, purple-spotted lip. The leaves are less than four inches long; the flower stalk is a foot high.

Silver Slipper: White lip; dull yellow petals.

Orchis

Showy Orchis has three to ten flowers in a terminal spike. (Moccasins and Slippers, you noted, have one or a few *solitary* flowers not in a cluster.) Each flower is fragrant, about an inch long, and purple, mixed with lighter purple and white. At the base is a spur; sepals and petals form a hood. The two dark, shiny leaves are near the base of the stem and are about six inches long and three wide. It blooms in spring in rich, damp woods westward to Dakota and Missouri. Too many pests attack it to make it an easy plant in the home garden.

One-leaf Orchis has a few half-inch flowers on a stalk about ten inches high. Each flower has a white spur, lilac sepals, and pink petals. The single leaf is three inches or less long, round and smooth. It grows only in cold swamps and damp woods.

Tall Leafy Green Orchis has many small, yellowish flowers on a stout stem that grows up to three feet. It grows in cold northern bogs west to Oregon.

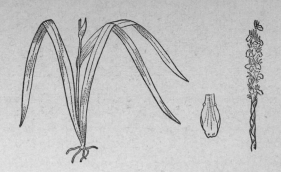

REIN-ORCHIDS

These belong to the genus *Habenaria* (Ha-ben-*nay*-ree-uh), the name meaning strap or rein and referring to the shape of the flower. Generally, the plants are a foot high. The flowers are greenish-white, about a half-inch long and in a cylindric head. They grow in cold, damp woods and bogs. They are not very showy, but these small natives make an interesting conversation piece in a moist rock garden or wild garden.

One-leaf Rein-Orchid: Nine inches tall; one leaf.
Club-spur Rein-Orchid: Few flowers on a tall stalk.
Lesser Pad-leaf Orchid: Leafless stalk a foot tall.
White Rein-Orchid: Long, slender flower head.

Ladies' Tresses

Like the Rein-orchids, the Ladies' Tresses (shown above) are small flowers grouped at the top of a prominent stalk. They are, however, in irregularly spiraled or twisted rows. Their generic name, *spiranthes* (spy-*ranth*-ees), means coils or twisted stalks. All are a foot tall, more or less, and partial to bogs or wet grasslands.

Autumn Ladies' Tresses: Small white flowers in three or four spirals on a leafy stalk six to twelve inches high.
Green-eyed: White flowers with a bright green spot on the lip. Evergreen leaves.
Spring: White flowers, a quarter-inch long, with a yellow stripe on the lip.

FRINGE ORCHIDS

The ten species of Fringe Orchids in North America are known for the delicate fringes on their petals. Their stems are tall, up to four feet, and leafy. Many small flowers appear on an open spike; each has a spur that is longer than the lip. Bracts, like leaves, extend beyond and under the flowers. Usually they prefer moist thickets, bogs, and damp meadows, and are widely distributed through the country. Most of them bloom in early summer.

Their names indicate something about their color and size: White Fringe, Orange Fringe, Lesser Orange Fringe, Purple Fringe, Purple Fanlip, Lesser Purple Fringe, Prairie Fringe, Meadow Fringe.

Especially interesting is the Larger Purple Fringe Orchid, whose fan-shaped lip and inch-long spur are so made that only large butterflies and small moths can enter to get the nectar and, in doing so, to pollinate the flower.

Coral-roots

Intriguing plants, these, that have no leaves, although their purplish to brownish or reddish stalks, which are about a foot tall, carry a few scales. Their tissues lack chlorophyll, and these saprophytes get all their food from humus at their roots. It is useless to try to transplant them. The underground stems resemble white coral.

Striped Coral-root is the largest—nine to eighteen inches. The many, small, half-inch flowers, in a raceme at the top, have purple stripes on the bronzy sepals, petals, and lip. Look for it in cool northern woods.

Autumn Coral-root has tiny, almost closed flowers. The white lip has purple spots.

Much the same are Northern Coral-root (yellow-green flowers) ; Southern Coral-root (pale yellow) ; and Summer Coral-root. All have foot-high flower stalks and white, purple-spotted lips.

WHITTIER: *Nature speaks in symbols and in signs.*

WATER-LILIES

You can easily identify the Water-Lilies. From the slime of ponds and slow streams arise these aristocrats, their flowers pristinely white or pure pink, their clean leaves a bright and handsome green. Some bloom by day, some introduced ones by night.

White Water-Lily has fragrant white (or pale pink) floating flowers, three to six inches across. It has many petals but only four sepals. The pistils (or carpels) unite into a ball-shaped ovary, at the top of which is a whorl of stigmas. The fruit matures after pollination by certain flies and bees and after the flower stalk is withdrawn to the bottom. The flower, found in the eastern part of the country as far west as Kansas, opens in morning and early afternoons when its special insects are near. The floating leaves are nearly a foot wide.

Similar to it is the Tuberous White Water-Lily, which has many thick tubers and white flowers four to nine inches across, only slightly fragrant. The foot-wide leaves are slightly hairy underneath.

In the north grows the small White Water-Lily, whose white flowers are an inch or two broad and whose leaves are oblong or oval, about three inches long and two wide.

Along the eastern coast is the Smaller White Water-Lily, notable because the underside of the leaf is dark red-purple.

41

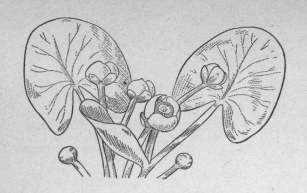

POND-LILIES

Spatterdock, or Large Yellow Pond-Lily, is typical of our dozen varieties of Pond-Lilies, which are close relatives of Water-Lilies. It is one of our favorites. It is pictured above.

The yellow flowers (sometimes green on the outside) are about three inches across. The petals are small, but the five or six sepals are leathery, concave, and outstanding. The leaves, almost oval, and heart-shaped at the base, are five to ten inches broad and somewhat longer. The stems are long. Quite noticeable in the center of the flower is the disk at the tip of the united pistils; from it radiate the stigmas. The plant grows in the eastern half of the country along muddy banks in still water. It blooms from spring to summer. Cowlily is another name for it.

Small Yellow Pond-Lily has inch-wide flowers, three-inch leaves, and a later blossoming period.

Indian Pond-Lily, which grows from South Dakota to California, has reddish flowers up to five inches wide.

American-Lotus, another of the Water-Lily cousins, carries its pale yellow flowers, four to eight inches wide, high above the surface of the slow streams and lakes where it grows. The pistils, which mature ahead of the stamens, are in pits in a half-round cup. The leaves, a foot or two across, arise from thick root-stocks, which Indians liked to eat.

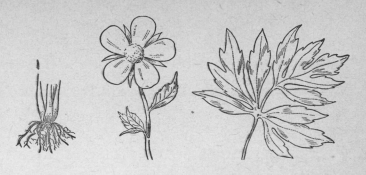

BUTTERCUPS

The Buttercup (or Crowfoot) family, a large one that includes the Buttercups, Hepatica, Anemone, Marsh-Marigold, Columbine, and others, have these character-istics: Separated flower parts, few or no petals, highly colored sepals that look like petals, and many stamens. Another clue to their group identity (one that does not always hold true) is given by the genus name of some of them, *Ranunculus* (ra-*nun*-kew-lus), which means little frog and implies that they live in marshy or wet places.

Among these is the Tall Buttercup, whose inch-wide, waxy yellow flowers brighten fields as far west as Kansas summerlong. Its common name derives from its height of two or three feet. Its leaves are deeply lobed and as broad as they are long. The plant is many-branched, erect, and hairy. It has five glistening petals and five spreading sepals. It and twenty-odd others are natives of Europe, and tend to be weedy.

Like it is Creeping Buttercup. Its stems root at the nodes and form big colonies. It blooms from May to July in wet ground and along roadsides in a wide area.

Bulblet Buttercup is shorter (twelve to eighteen inches). Its leaves are less deeply cut and narrower.

Swamp Buttercup (shown above) bears bright yellow, inch-wide flowers on arching, hairy stems. The leaves have three-toothed leaflets. It lives in swamps and thickets.

In the West you find Sagebrush Buttercup (also with waxy yellow blooms and three-cleft leaves) and the Large-Flowered Buttercup, a tall species.

43

ANEMONES

Usually the Anemones have sepals—white, pink, or lavender—instead of petals, and hairy stems and leaves. You find them mostly in open woods in spring and early summer. There is a myth that these delicate, handsome things arose from tears that Venus shed on the death of Adonis.

Outstanding among the twenty-some species is the Pasqueflower, a lavender-blue beauty that visits open woods and grasslands from Wisconsin to Texas and westward in early spring. Its petals are obsolete, but it has five or seven sepals an inch long. The many pistils produce feathery fruits. The very hairy stems are a foot high, more or less. The leaves are hairy, basal, and divided.

Wood Anemone is the smallest of the wild Anemones. Its one-inch flowers grow on stalks that are four to eight inches high and have in the middle a whorl of sharply cut bracts. The five or seven sepals are white or fringed with lavender. The deeply cut leaves are like the bracts, but larger. You find this shy flower in early spring in wet woodlands west to Minnesota. Broad-leaf Anemone has stem leaves without stalks, or sessile. The white flowers are an inch and a half across. The leaves are broad and cut-toothed. It flowers in late spring in open woods west to Colorado.

Tall Anemone has long-stalked stem leaves, two or three feet high with whorls of indented bracts. The five sepals are greenish-white. The many woolly pistils are in a thimble-shaped group. It likes dry woods and slopes westward to Kansas.

Zephyr Anemone likes the western mountains. It has clusters of deep yellow flowers on long stems.

Carolina Anemone beautifies the eastern three-fourths of the country with big purple flowers in early spring.

Rue Anemone (not a true Anemone) is entirely smooth and up to ten inches tall. Its wiry stems spring from a cluster of tuberous roots. The white or pink sepals are three-fourths inch wide. The grouped flowers arise from a whorl of bracts. Leaves appear after the flowers and are compound three times, somewhat like the Meadow-Rue. It favors open woods in the eastern half.

MARSH-MARIGOLD

One of of our loveliest wild flowers is the bright yellow Marsh Marigold, which grows in wet places in the Northeast and Midwest and is known also as Cowslip. A key characteristic is its thick, hollow stalk, up to two feet tall, which carries shiny green and heart-shaped leaves. The many flowers are about one inch across and have five sepals. The pistils are in a whorl and produce many seeds because insects have to climb all around to get at the several nectar glands. It is well worth having in your wild garden. You could cook the leaves for greens—if you must.

Virgin's Bower

Virgin's Bower is one of those plants that are too easy to take for granted. On long vines that twine on banks, other plants, and fences, appear in late summer lacy, leafy panicles of small white flowers, which later produce one-seeded, plumy-tailed fruits. Leaves are attractive, too: They are smooth, opposite, compound, and cut into three leaflets. If you have a damp place that needs a screen, try Virgin's Bower.

Purple Virgin's Bower has short vines and large, single purple flowers, in which the sepals look like petals. It grows in the Eastern half of the country in rocky places. The leaves have three leaflets on slender stalks. The outer stamens are so broad they might be taken for petals.

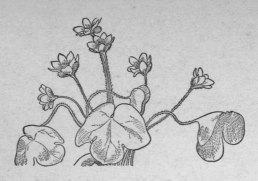

THE HEPATICAS

Even before the snow leaves the woodsides in the East and Midwest you can find (but please do not pick!) the dainty white, pink, lavender, or blue Hepatica. The half-inch flowers are on thin, hairy stalks about six inches high, and appear before the new leaves start growing. The old rounded, rusty-red leaves stay through the winter to protect the plant. There are up to ten colored sepals. Petals are obsolete, but on the fuzzy stalk, just behind the flower, are three bracts that look like sepals and a calyx.

Sharp-lobe Hepatica, more abundant in the East, has showier flower, and sharper leaf lobes. Often its flowers are *dioecious* (dye-oh-*ee-shus*) —male and female flowers are produced on different plants. It is illustrated above. Another name for Hepatica is Liverleaf.

Blue-eyed Grass

These cousins of the noble Iris are mostly low tufts of violet-blue, star-shaped, half-inch flowers on wiry stalks a foot or less high. The leaves are like grass. In spring and summer these graceful plants color meadows a light blue for a few hours when the sun is brightest; the next day a new crop takes their place. The twenty-odd species are much alike in habit, except two kinds, which are rose, red, purple, and which grow in the South and West.

A picture of this pretty flower is on page 138.

MEADOW-RUE

This is a tall flower, one "which has not yet ascended the evolutionary scale high enough to economize its pollen by making insects carry it invariably" and so "overtops surrounding vegetation to take advantage of every breeze that blows."

On leafy stalks that sometimes reach ten feet, Tall Meadow-Rue produces masses of greenish-white flowers, that are individually insignificant but handsome in their large panicles. The lacy, delicate, compound leaves are divided into threes; the leaflets are rounded. It occurs in summer in moist thickets, meadows, and roadsides, west to Ohio and southward.

Bugbane

What's in a name? Bugbanes are named that because of their rank smell and as a translation of the genus name, *Cimicifuga* (sim-is-*siff*-you-guh), which means insect-repelling; Mountain Rattlebox because the dry seeds rattle; Fairy-candles because of the long, slender, airy racemes of small white flowers; and Cohosh I know not why.

The six American species are alike in having leafy stalks four or six feet tall; large, coarse, sharp-toothed leaves; petal-like sepals that fall early; minute petals; and conspicuous stamens that give a fluffy look.

Black Cohosh, or Fairy-candles, sometimes has flower groups three feet long in summer. It grows from Maine to Wisconsin and Missouri on wooded slopes.

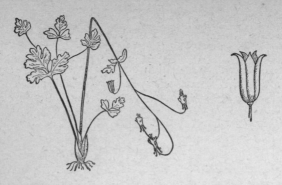

THE COLUMBINES

Beloved in woods and meadows countrywide and highly popular in their hybrid forms in nearly everyone's garden are the Columbines or *Aquilegia* (akwill-*ee*-jee-uh), which means eagle-like. The key features are the long slender spurs (which produce the nectar), and the cornucopia shape of the five petals.

Eastern Columbine has red flowers, one to two inches long, with a yellow face, beyond which the stamens extend. The five sepals are small and like petals; the five petals extend backward to form the spur. Flower stalks are about two feet tall. As in all Columbines, the lacy leaves are doubly compounded in threes, with lobed, rounded leaflets. It is at home among shady rocks and banks and is easy to cultivate in almost any kind of soil. It blooms in May and June.

Several other red Columbines (Southern, Scarlet, Formosa, and California, among them) differ mainly in name and home and maybe in size. Hummingbirds love them.

Small-flowered Columbine has small blue or purple flowers and lives in woods and meadows west of the Dakotas.

Long-spurred Blue Columbine is Colorado's state flower. Its spurs are two inches long, or more.

The picture above of the Columbine shows details of the plant so you can identify it, but does not do full justice to this fairy flower.

THE LARKSPURS

Simpler, smaller, and less showy than their garden sisters, the Delphiniums, are the wild Larkspurs, whose corolla (like that of the Columbines) has become specialized into a spur. Most of our forty species are blue or lavender; all contain a poisonous element. They thrive in open places and are not particular as to place or soil.

Spring Larkspur, a native of the Midland States, is white or blue or lavender and about a foot high. It is illustrated above. The inch-long flowers are in a loose, prominent cylinder. The petals are insignificant; one of the five sepals makes a cone-shaped spur. The leaves are cut into very slender lobes. It is planted sometimes for its early spring flowers—but its nature is indicated by the name some Midwesterners give it, Staggerweed.

Tall Larkspur carries many small lavender-blue flowers on a slender, leafy stalk two to six feet tall. It blooms late, and is less handsome than some of the others.

Prairie Larkspur, which grows in the West, has off-white flowers and narrow leaf segments.

Scarlet Larkspur, in the Far West, has a thick, erect stem up to six feet tall and thick, lance-like leaves six inches wide. The bright flowers have long spurs and yellowish sepals, and are in open racemes.

Red Larkspur, also a Westerner and mountaineer, has almost leafless stems a foot or two high. Both have a red calyx and yellow corolla.

Poisonweed has long cylinders of handsome blue flowers, but cattlemen in the West abhor it for its danger to cattle.

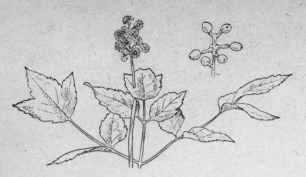

THE BANEBERRIES

These differ from the Bugbanes primarily in having flower cylinders only a few inches long on stalks about two feet high. The berries are the conspicuous mark.

White Baneberry produces white poisonous berries, purple-tipped, on a bright red, thick stalk. The flowers are small and white, in a broad raceme at the tips of the stalks. The petals are narrow. The leaves are large and sharply pointed and have several leaflets. Stamens are prominent. It blooms in spring on wooded slopes west to Dakota. It is shown above.

Red Baneberry has red berries on slender stalks.

Monkshood

These members of the Buttercup family have hoods or helmets formed by the enlargement of one of the five sepals—hence the name.

Summer Aconite (or Wild Monkshood) has one-inch violet-blue flowers at the branch tips of slender leafy stems two to four feet long. It is at home in damp thickets over the eastern half of the country.

Many others of the fifty genera of Crowfoot or Buttercup family are worth investigating; among them are outstanding medicinal and flower-garden plants. Although they have many variations, remember that all have separate flower parts, few petals but showy sepals, and many stamens. Or, as another help in identification, consider them in terms of Columbine, which you know better.

BARBERRY FAMILY

May-Apple (above) has a single, white, nodding, two-inch flower that comes in May and develops into a sweet yellow "apple" that pigs and boys like to eat when it is fully ripe. From the long, thick, poisonous underground stems come twisted spears that unfold to leaves as much as a foot across and cut deeply into coarse, toothed lobes. The flower stems arise from different rootstocks and usually have one to three large leaves of their own. The flower has six to nine petals and twice that many stamens. It grows in damp, open woods as far west as Minnesota and South to Florida and Texas. It spreads too rapidly to have in any except large wild gardens.

Twinleaf has white, inch-wide flowers on leafless stems that rise right out of the ground. The heart-shaped leaves, also growing directly from the ground, are deeply cleft into two wings and are about four inches wide and six inches long. The plant is six or eight inches high, but when its single carpel (or pistil) matures to a dry, pear-shaped fruit, it grows to eighteen inches or so. The flowers last only a day and come in April and May in rich woods westward to Wisconsin and south to Tennessee.

Another of the thirty species of the Barberry (or May-Apple) family is the Blue Cohosh, or Papoose-root. Instead of large leaves, however, it has compound leaves cut into nine leaflets, a terminal group of small, purplish-green flowers. The three-foot stem grows from thick rootstocks. It blossoms in May in fertile woods.

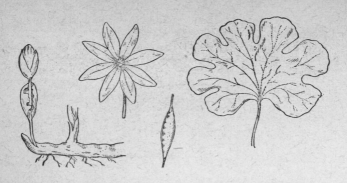

BLOODROOT AND POPPIES

Bloodroot, one of our favorite flowers, gets its name from the red juice in its thick underground stem. Indians once used it for war paint.

All Poppies (of which Bloodroot is one) have a cloudy or milky juice. Other family features are large, delicate flowers that have petals in fours and a single pistil that matures to a many-sided dry fruit. Stamens are many.

The Bloodroot's solitary white or pinkish flower, an inch or so across and short-lived, has eight to sixteen spoon-shaped petals in two or three rows. As the flower stalk penetrates the ground in early spring, a young leaf clasps it tightly to protect it against the cold. The leaves are gray-green, broad, and round-lobed. It is native to the East, but many wild-gardeners elsewhere like it.

Gold-Poppy has yellow juice, four bright yellow petals, a leafy stalk about a foot high, and one pistil that ripens into a fuzzy fruit. It grows in woods in the East and Midwest and blooms in spring.

California-Poppy, the pride and the state flower of California, bears one glowing orange, copper, or yellow flower, an inch to four inches across, on stems up to two feet tall. It has small, fleshy, gray-green leaves.

Field Poppy is a hairy plant one or two feet high. Its showy red flowers are three inches across.

Among the half-dozen kinds of Prickly-Poppies, all with spiny leaves and yellow juice, are the handsome, yellow, Smooth Prickly-Poppy and Mexican Prickly-Poppy. Both grow far south, and southwestward.

THE DICENTRAS

You know the Dutchman's Breeches by the spreading spurs formed at the base of the flower by the two reflexing outer petals. If you are imaginative, you see a resemblance to a pair of breeches. Or, you might think they look like small hearts—hence another common name for them, Whitehearts. At any rate, they belong to the Fumeroot, or Fumitory, family, and the genus *Dicentra* (dye-*sent*-rah), meaning two-spurred. A fellow member of that genus is the familiar Bleeding-heart, a favorite in old-fashioned gardens.

Dutchman's Breeches has a single leafless arching stalk, higher than the leaves, that carries four to ten nodding flowers in a one-sided cluster. Each flower has a pair of scaly sepals and four irregular petals, white or pale pink, with a yellow tip. The leaves are smooth, lacy, and pale underneath. It grows from a nobby bulb and blooms in early spring in deep, moist, rich woods from New England to Minnesota, south to North Carolina and Missouri. In the wild garden, alas, it blooms only sparsely.

Squirrel Corn is much the same, with about the same geographic distribution, except that its spurs are short, rounded, and not spreading. The fragrant flowers are greenish-white or white with a pink or purplish tinge. The smaller petals have yellowish crests. Its name derives from its small yellow tubers.

Wild Bleeding-heart has pink flowers and is much taller (to two feet) than the preceding. Its leaves also are basal and larger. It blossoms from May to early fall.

53

CROSS-BEARERS

Remember this about the large family that bears the name of Mustard or Cress or *Cruciferae* (krew-*siff*-er-ee, meaning cross-bearer), or *Brassicaceae* (brass-ih-*kay*-see-ee, meaning cabbage) : Nearly always are the four petals arranged in opposite pairs like a cross; four of the six stamens are longer than the others and prominently placed. Among the hundreds of species of cross-bearers are vegetables like mustard, cabbage, cauliflower, radish.

Take Shepherd's Purse (illustrated above) as an example. Many botanists flatly call it a common, every-day weed, and let it go at that. It is no great beauty, but it is interesting to us as a key to the whole group. It grows about a foot high. It has racemes of tiny, white flowers that have four petals and bear flat, three-cornered pods or boxes, as indicated in the generic name *Capsella,* which means little box. The leaves at the base are rough, deeply cut, and in a cluster.

Yellow Rocket inhabits roadsides and waste places in April and May. Its small, bright yellow flowers are in racemes at the top of a two-foot angled stem. The lower leaves are five inches long, lobed, and with stalks.

Bittercress has half-inch flowers in slender groups and inch-long seed pods. Roots are tubers. Lavender Bittercress grows about a foot high and has a hairy stalk and coarse leaves. It grows in the North central states.

Crinkle-root has few half-inch, white or pale pink flowers on hairy stalks about a foot tall. It grows from fleshy underground stems in early spring. It prefers woods.

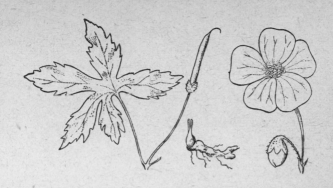

GERANIUM

The Wild Geraniums, or Cranesbill, differ from the house Geraniums you know so well in having less fleshy stems, more regular flowers, and more cuts or divisions in the leaves. Cultivated Geraniums are tropical and semi-tropical species of the genus Pelargonium. Our sixty-odd species of wild Geraniums have a peculiar beak-like seed capsule that resembles a crane's bill (hence the name; "geranium" means crane). The flowers, usually purplish but sometimes rose or white, range from one-fourth inch across to two inches. The leaves have five to nine lobes.

Outstanding is the Wild Geranium, which is also known as Wood Geranium or Spotted Cranesbill and which has thick rootstocks and three- to five-parted leaves. Its one-inch, rose-lavender flowers are delicately veined and grow at the tip of upright leafy stalks that are one or two feet tall. Bud and stem are hairy. Look for it in woods from Maine to Nebraska, it blooms from April to July. It is a good plant for wild gardens.

Herb Robert has half-inch rose-lavender flowers on slender, weak, forked stalks a foot high. The broad, compound leaves, cut into three toothed leaflets, have a pleasant musk odor. It blooms May to October. Stems and leaves become red and red-splotched later in the year. It occurs in rocky woods from New England west to Minnesota and Missouri. It is called Red Robin sometimes; some people believe it was named after Robin Hood or Saint Robert, founder of the Cistercian Order.

THE JEWEL-WEEDS

In damp places in the eastern half of the country one finds all summer long the bright, red-spotted, orange-yellow, pouched Jewel-weeds, whose names tell their features: Jewel-weed, because dew drops on their toothed, two-inch stalked leaves glisten like silvery gems; Impatiens, Touch-me-Not, and Snapweed because the fruit capsule, when touched, explodes.

Spotted Jewel-weed, two to six feet high, has reddish-brown spots on the orange-yellow flowers, which appear in clusters or singly over the many succulent branches. One of the three sepals is large, like a petal, and spurred; two of the three petals are cleft into lobes. The leaves are egg-shaped or oval and coarsely toothed. It is common in damp, shady places. Its juice is good for ivy poisoning.

Pale Jewel-weed, with light yellow flowers and a wider and shorter spur sepal, is larger and stouter and more sparingly spotted. Norton's Jewel-weed, shown above, grows farther west.

In one of the interesting leaflets he has prepared for the Wild Flower Preservation Society, Dr. P. L. Ricker writes: "Nature has many types of devices for the dispersal of seeds. Some seeds are carried into the ground by ants; some are dropped without any help and germinate, if at all, where they fall; some are carried by the wind on wings or small parachutes, some have spines or hooks for attaching themselves to animals or to man; some are eaten, carried and dropped by birds; some float on the water; some stick to damp dirt on the feet of animals and man."

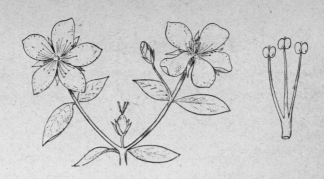

SEVERAL SAINTS

All fifty-five of our St. Johnsworts have yellow or bronzy flowers; small, black-dotted leaves; and many stamens and a few united pistils. They tend to be shrubby plants about two feet tall. They blossom in summer and are known in nearly all parts of the country, usually in wooded, rocky, rather poor soil.

The name originated long ago when people connected the flower with the observance of St. John's Day, June 24.

Two, which grow as far west as Texas, have four petals, cross-like: St. Andrews-cross is a low, many-branched, woody-stemmed plant with many small flowers in the upper leaf axils. St. Peterswort is taller and puts forth its brighter yellow flowers in terminal groups.

The others have five sepals and five petals:

Great St. Johnswort: Many one- to two-inch flowers in sparse clusters at the branch tips on a three-foot, leafy stalk. It is illustrated above. It grows west of New England.

Golden St. Johnswort: Few or single flowers on shrubby branches up to four feet high.

Common St. Johnswort (or Klamathweed) : Conspicuous black dots on leaves and flowers. It is very leafy, about two feet high, and narrow-leaved.

Straggling St. Johnswort: Ribbon-like leaves.

Of another genus is the Common Marsh St. Johnswort, which has pink flowers, smooth, erect, and reddish stems, and many oblong, black-spotted leaves.

THE VIOLETS

The world has many hundreds of species of Violets, of which several hundred grow in the United States. It is not hard to identify them as a group, for they are all small plants with a distinct butterfly, or bilateral, shape: Two side petals are narrow; two upper petals are usually erect; those four usually have stripes of a bright color to guide insects to the nectar inside; and the fifth petal, the lowest and largest, has a hollow spur extending backward.

Some Violets have "beards" or hairs on the side and bottom petals to keep out rain and give insects a place to land.

Many Violets later in summer produce a second set of inconspicuous flowers that do not open and do not need insects to transfer pollen so seed can be formed.

Some Violets have leafy stems; some are stemless—that is, the flowers and leaves rise directly from a rootstock. Our wild Violets are closely related to Pansies, Violas, and Johnny-Jump-Ups, which every gardener knows and loves. One more interesting detail about Violets: They hybridize freely with each other, forming vigorous new forms; some, indeed, spread so rapidly that you almost can consider them weedy. Violets are easy to transplant. Because of their two sets of flowers, you need not hesitate to pick violets if you do not disturb the roots.

Those paragraphs refer to Violets in general. But Christine and I felt we needed more than that so we could tell one species from another. We found, though, that some guides were a little too involved, so we started our own rule-of-thumb list, in which we avoided too technical details and too general facts, such as that most Violets like cool, moist, wooded slopes, they grow about a foot high, and the flower is about an inch across. We paid most attention to color and shape of leaf.

Among those of violet-purple-blue-lavender colors are:
Birdfoot (shown at the top of the next page): Two upper petals dark violet; three lower lilac-purple. Fan-shaped leaves, with many narrow divisions.

Meadow: Corolla deep violet; greenish yellow or white at center; long stalks; wide, heart-shaped leaves.

Broadleaf Wood Violet: Young leaves are purple-tinged.

Longspur: Lavender; heart-shaped leaves; leafy-stems; flowers in axils of leafy bracts.

Northern Blue: Stemless; blue; slightly hairy.

Northern Bog: Smooth; in cold bogs and banks.

Marsh Blue: Many violet-blue flowers; throat darker; long stems.

Ovate-leaf: Violet-purple; dry fields and hillsides.

Arrowleaf: L a r g e , a r r o w - shaped leaves; profuse bloomer.

Coast: Leaves deeply divided in threes.

Prairie: Sharply cut leaves; striking, violet flowers.

Confederate (illustrated on page 60): One of the handsomest; many flowers more than an inch wide; grayish color; bright, violet-blue veins on petals.

LeConte's: Smooth foliage; white center in flowers.

Marsh: Pale lilac; dark veins; creeping; four inches tall; grows in north.

Great-spurred: Stemless; enlarged spurs; pale violet; northern localities.

White Violets

Canada: Leaf-stemmed; foot high; white flowers with yellow eye, lilac shading on back; heart-shaped leaves.

Sweet White: Fragrant; lower petals twisted; stems red-tinged.

Northern White: Hairy stems; fragrant; reddish tinge.

Water: Narrow lance leaves; common.

YELLOW VIOLETS

Smooth Yellow: Leafy stemmed; yellow flowers in axils of leafy bracts; heart-shaped leaves. Widespread.

Hastata: Halberd-shaped leaves.

Yellow Roundleaf: Stemless; large leaves close to the ground.

Downy Yellow: Tall; hairy, toothed leaves; small golden flowers, purple-veined.

Several Colors
(Mostly in West and Midwest)

Pine: Petals yellow, purple in back; leaves cleft.

Yellow Pansy: Upper petals brown; purple veins.

Western Heartsease: White, violet, yellow; purple veins.

Beckwith's: Upper petals deep purple; others white or light blue, purple-veined; yellowish base.

Pale Violet: Handsome; heart-shaped leaves; white to lavender flowers, purple-striped.

The Violet (or Viola) family comprises fifteen genera, some of which (as a point of passing interest) are shrubs or trees. One should not confuse them with African-Violet or Dog-tooth-Violet, which belong to different families and have only the name in common.

Most violets are excellent subjects for the wild garden. Many are quite undemanding, although they prefer part shade and good soil.

MILKWORTS

Sometimes the Milkworts are called Candyroots because of the wintergreen-like flavor of the roots. All of our sixty-odd species are less than a foot tall and have attractive bilateral flowers, in which two of five sepals are enlarged, like petals, and all three petals form a tube.

Purple Milkwort (illustrated right) has tiny, rosy-purple, or greenish flowers in small but dense clusters on leafy stems about eight inches high. You find it in summer in damp meadows or sandy ground through the East. Often the five unequal sepals are pink, three petals are yellowish, inconspicuous, and united, and two large wing petals are purplish. The flower heads are oblong and about a third of an inch thick. The common name and the scientific name, *Polygala* ("much milk") refer to the old idea that cows gave more milk if they ate Milkwort.

Yellow Milkwort has tiny orange-yellow flowers in dense, rounded spikes on leafy stems. It has a more southerly range.

Racemed Milkwort carries its purple or rose flowers in a terminal raceme on erect, short stems.

Marsh Milkwort occurs widely in swamps and meadows. It stands erect to show off its thick heads of white, off-green, or purple flower. The dull green leaves are in whorls of four.

Gay-wings is a cheerful plant six inches tall. Its flowers are purple with a pink tube and a crest of dull gold. They are a half inch long and appear one to four at a time in axils of leafy bracts. They like cool, rich woods.

THE SPURGES

These are a large, important group of rather small plants, which have milky juice and from one or another of which we get rubber, tapioca, castor oil, and other drugs.

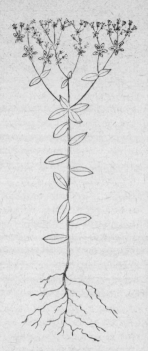

Snow - on - the - Mountain has nondescript greenish flowers below which are bright-green, white-margined bracts in pairs or whorls of three or more. These bracts give it distinction. The erect stems, two or three feet high, have many green, smooth leaves. A native of the West and Midwest, it is often seen in gardens in the East. It blooms in summer and fall, and inhabits dry grasslands. Mr. Horn's drawing of it appears at the right of this page.

White Spurge has many small, narrow leaves on straight, two-foot stems, at the top of which is an umbel of inconspicuous white flowers—actually a white collection of bracts. Leaves are ribbon-like.

Not for gardens are several weedy Spurges, which, however, serve to cover and redeem waste places. Like the others, they have inconspicuous flowers but a group of leaf-like bracts, almost like petals, of yellow-green or yellow. Some have reddish foliage.

Among the two hundred and fifty widely distributed genera of Spurge are herbs, shrubs, and trees. If you examine carefully the Poinsettia, which you very likely have in your home at Christmas time, you will get a clue to many of the Spurges—the red, showy parts that you might think are the flower, are really leaf-like bracts; the flowers are the tiny, green "buttons" in the middle.

THE PINKS

Satisfactory is as good as any word for the Pinks, which are undemanding, pretty, and sometimes handsome flowers. The Pink family includes Campions, Dianthus ("Jove's flower"), Silene, Sweet William, Catchfly.

The Campions, mostly European immigrants, belong to the genus *Lychnis* (*lik*-niss), which means lamp—a detail that might help you in identifying them, for they are bright in color and, just under the petals, the five sepals unite into a noticeable lamp-shaped or bell-shaped structure.

Cuckoo-flower has s l e n d e r, erect stems, a foot or two high, somewhat hairy and sticky. The flowers are pink, blue, purplish, or white, about an inch broad, and in many-flowered panicles at the top of the stems. The five petals are ragged and seem to have narrow claws. You find it in the East in July and August in moist fields and waste places. Another name is Ragged-Robin.

White Campion opens at night, when moths are attracted to its glistening white flowers. Staminate and pistillate flowers are on separate plants. A foot or two high, the branchy plants are sticky and hairy.

Starry Campion—or Star Silene—has many white, fringed flowers less than an inch across. The sepals form a hairy bell. The leaves, on two-foot stems, are in "wheels" of four. It blooms in summer in east-central areas. A picture of it appears above.

Mullein-pink has dense white wool on its two-foot stems and leaves. Its flowers are crimson and one inch across. It has made itself at home in many waste places.

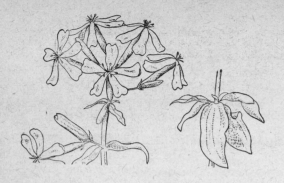

CATCHFLY

Silene (sye-*lee*-nee) is the generic name of a group of lovely plants that merit better names than Catchfly.

Red Catchfly (Firepink or Silene Virginica) has bright red flowers nearly two inches across. The sepals form a sticky tube. The five petals are toothed at the tip. The stem is about a foot long, branching, and hairy. It blooms in spring and summer in eastern localities in dry woods and slopes. It is worth trying in a wild garden, although pests attack it.

Pink Catchfly has pink petals; the sepals form a long, hairy tube. The plant is low and tufted.

Corn Cockle has showy red or purple flowers. The five flaring petals are two inches across. It has hairy, erect stems up to three feet tall. It is common everywhere in fields and waste places. It has narrow leaves about four inches long.

Bouncing Bet (above) has pale pink flowers in dense clusters, and somewhat notched. It is a foot or two high, with a few leafy branches. Its juice lathers in water.

Deptford Pink is smooth, slender, and about a foot tall. Its small, pink flowers have pale dots and come in summer in flat-topped groups. Its erect, ribbony leaves are little more than an inch long.

Rock Sandwort has white flowers, rounded at the tip. The tufted stems are eight inches or so tall. Leaves are thin. It blooms in summer in dry places.

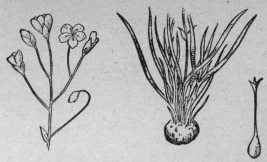

SPRING BEAUTY

These are members of the Portulaca or Purslane family and are small, delicate, white or pink flowers that beautify open woods in all parts of the country. They grow on low, weak stems from deep-placed tubers and have two ribbon- or lance-shaped basal leaves. The flowers are in loose terminal racemes and come in March to May.

Common Spring Beauty (above) has half-inch flowers, white or pink with deeper pink veining. Its stem is several inches high, and leaves are long and narrow. It appears in spring in moist open woods.

The Portulacas, a small family, are all showy, fleshy, and supple. All are sun-lovers, and several annuals among them are garden favorites, although the flowers tend to be short-lived. Illustrated above is Hairy Portulaca, which likes sunny fencerows and roadsides through the Midwest south to Texas. It displays fleshy, almost cylindric leaves and white, pink, orange, or red flowers.

POKE BERRY

The Poke Berry, or Poke Weed, is one of a small family of five species. They are coarse, tall weeds, as high as twelve feet, with branched groups of small, white flowers that have no petals. The Poke Berry has large poisonous roots and stout stems. The leaves are a foot or so long. It grows in open woods, thickets, and pastures. The deep purple berries were once used to make ink; birds like them. The young shoots (be careful not to get any root) are often cooked as spring greens.

Narrowleaf Umbrellawort has thick, ribbony leaves and panicles of purple flowers. It is an upstanding plant with sizable leaves and forking stems. It grows in the Midwest and is one of the three hundred members of the Four-o'clock family, along with the Common Four-o'clock, Wishbonebush, and the Sand-verbenas. One feature of the Four-o'clocks is that their flowers open with clocklike regularity in late afternoon.

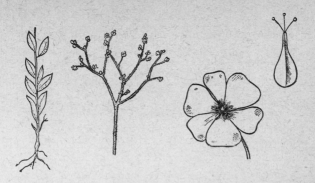

THE BUCKWHEATS

The Umbrellaplants are the largest and handsomest of the Buckwheats, a widely distributed family in which the colorful calyx has usurped the corolla's business. The flowers usually are white or pink, but sometimes yellow.

The one illustrated above is the Annual Umbrellaplant, which grows in the Midwest.

Yellow Umbrellaplant is white, woolly, and a foot tall. The leaves are three inches or less long and clustered near the base. The single flower stalk carries a whorl of leaves at the top and a bunch of yellow flowers.

James Umbrellaplant has pink or white flowers and grows on the western plains.

Desert Trumpet has a loose cluster of small, off-yellow flowers and thickened stems. It likes arid places in the West.

Wild Buckwheat grows in the Southeast. It has white flowers and whorled leaves.

Better known in the East are three other and different species of Buckwheat.

Lady's Thumb is a water plant. Its pink flowers form a rounded cluster. Its oblong leaves are unlobed and three inches long.

Jumpseed is known for the way the ripe fruits jump from the stalk when one touches them. It grows up to three feet and has white flowers spaced along a thin stalk.

Sand Jointweed has many tiny white or pink flowers in a group. Its jointed stems are less than a foot high.

WILD ROSES

Among the 1,200-odd species of the prized Rose family are Spireas, Blackberries, Raspberries, Dewberries, Strawberries, Avens, Cinquefoils, the aristocratic and cherished Hybrid Tea Roses, and the winsome Wild Roses—a varied, useful, and beautiful family whose members have in common flowers that are mostly radially symmetric and have many stamens. Mostly, also, they have five petals, and five sepals, which are borne on a disk.

Dwarf Wild Rose *(Rosa virginiana)* is most like the plants we usually think of as roses. It has five rosy petals and many stamens and pistils, which mature to one-seeded fruits inside the hollow calyx. The sepals are united to form an urn that becomes red and fleshy. Leaves are divided into five or nine toothed leaflets, which are sharply toothed and have long stalks. It has hooked thorns. It is found in summer through the eastern states in open or wooded swamps and sandy slopes. It grows to five feet and is bushy.

Pasture Rose *(Rosa humilis)* is only about half as high. Its flowers are two or three inches broad, few or solitary, and rose or pink, which fades after opening. It likes dry or rocky soil and blossoms in the eastern half of the country in May-July.

Sweetbrier—Eglantine to the poets—is six feet high or less. Its stout stems have backward-bending thorns.

Dog Rose has leaflets that are single-toothed.

Smooth Rose, less than four feet tall, has few thorns.

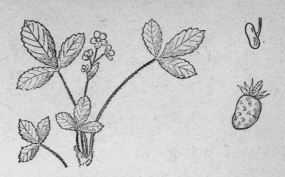

STRAWBERRIES

By their red, sweet fruits and their three long-stalked leaves you can tell another of the Rose family. Wild Strawberry, like the tame ones, produces delicious "berries" that actually are pulpy receptacles, on or in which are many separate seeds.

Wild Strawberry (or Virginia Strawberry) is a low plant with a few small flowers at the tip of a long stem. As in other Roses, it has many stamens and pistils. It is common throughout the East in late spring. It is shown in the drawing above.

Almost the same are Scarlet Strawberry in the West; Sand Strawberry, which is leathery and hairy; and Wood Strawberry. These, especially the last, and foreign species are the parents of our cultivated strawberries.

Avens

The Avens are the country cousins of the gardener's Geums. A distinguishing mark is that the pinnate leaves are divided into broad, toothed leaflets; the end leaf is the largest, and sometimes the larger leaflets of the basal leaves have tiny leaves among them.

Yellow Avens has golden, three-fourths-inch flowers on three-foot stems. It flowers in summer in moist woods.

White Avens is about two feet high, with a few white blossoms that are less attractive than the foliage.

Purple Avens have purple-brown flowers an inch broad.

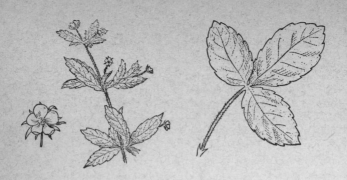

CINQUEFOILS

The Cinquefoils (*sink*-queh-foil) have five toothed leaf-lets that stick out sharply like the fingers of a hand. The flowers are five-petalled, yellow, purple, or white that resemble Strawberry blossoms. Many of the Cinquefoils dress up sandy waste places in a most accommodating way all summer. They are the largest non-shrubby group in the Rose family. Often their slender stems act as runners, instead of being upright.

Wine-leaf Cinquefoil makes a low tuft of three-part leaflets, which turn red in autumn. The white flowers are one-third of an inch wide and have many stamens and pistils. It likes rocks and gravel over much of the country.

Silver Cinquefoil, also tufted and low, has five to seven yellow petals, each a half inch long, and compound leaves composed of seven to twenty-five toothed leaflets, which are silvery underneath. It spreads by slender runners and grows in dry ground everywhere. It is upright and less than a foot high.

Sulphur Cinquefoil is erect, stout, hairy, and yellow.

The species shown at the top of the page is Rough Cinquefoil, which is rough, coarse, branching, and up to three feet tall. The flowers, less than one-half inch across, are in leafy clusters. The five petals are broad at the end. There appear to be ten sepals—actually there are five sepals and five bracts. A key mark is the three coarsely toothed leaflets into which the leaves are divided. It is common in dry places.

OTHER ROSES

The following flowers also are members of the Rose family because they all have (1) regular flowers; (2) alternate leaves with stipules like a pair of little blades at the base of the leafstalk; (3) generally five petals and at least ten stamens that are inserted in a cup. Such points, to repeat, are among the factors that determine the classification of plants—details of color, size of plants, habitat, and such can vary too much with changes in environment.

Dewdrop, a low, tufted plant that likes moist, acid soil and grows west to Minnesota and south to North Carolina, has two kinds of flowers. One set has small, white, starry, third-inch flowers borne singly or doubly on the slender stalks. The other flowers are small and hard to find near the ground; they are self-fertilizing, so they need no insects to spread their pollen. In this and the shape of the leaves they resemble Violets. Indeed, they are sometimes called Star-Violet. They are related closely to Raspberries and Blackberries. They grow in bogs and woods.

American Burnet stands three to five feet high and its compound leaves can be two feet long—a noble plant. Its small white flowers are in dense spikes. It grows in wet thickets and meadows west to Michigan and south to Georgia. It blossoms in early fall.

Bowman-root has white or pink narrow flowers on slender stalks. The plant grows to three feet in open woods in the Midwest and South. It blooms May to July.

Queen-of-the-Prairie is much in evidence in the Midwest; you cannot miss it, for it grows as high as eight feet and has leaves up to three feet long and divided into nine to twenty-seven parts. The small pink or purple flowers are in impressive panicles and are fragrant. It blossoms in summer in damp grasslands. Try it in your garden, if you have the space for it.

You find Meadow Sweet all summer in fields and meadows everywhere. It is small, shrubby, and attractive for its tip clusters of small flowers, which are white or pale pink and have a fuzzy look because of the many prominent stamens. The leaves are oval and toothed.

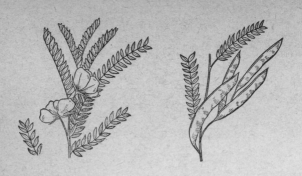

THE SENNAS

Most of our seventy-five kinds of Sennas have compound, pinnate leaves—leaves that, like a feather, have a middle axis from which fern-like leaflets diverge on both sides. Leaves of some of them will fold up when touched. The flowers, mostly yellow, are somewhat bilateral; the two parts are images of each other, as in the Pea. Another mark is the seed pod—long, tubular, and two-valved.

Partridge-Pea, an annual, has one-inch yellow flowers, purple spotted near the base, and borne in thin clusters in the leaf joints. It blooms from July to September. Stamens are purple and yellow. Seed pods are two inches long. The plant is about a foot or two high. You will not overlook the many pairs of narrow, oblong leaflets, each less than an inch long. It grows from Massachusetts to Minnesota south to Texas in open woods and dry ground. It is pictured above.

Among the other varieties of Senna are:

Large-flowered Sensitive Pea (to two feet tall; thirty or so tiny leaflets in each leaf); Florida Partridge-pea (purple sepals around the five yellow petals; very tall); Gulf Sensitive-pea (large yellow or white flowers).

Midland Wild-Senna, a perennial, has many yellow flowers in clusters at the tips of tall (four to six feet) stems. The pods are flat, many segmented, and about three inches long; they contain several seeds and split into two valves. It grows on gravelly slopes in the Midwest. It has larger leaflets and smaller flowers than the Partridge-Pea.

72

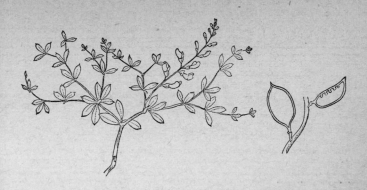

PEAS AND PULSE

You know, of course, that gardener's delight, the Sweet-pea—and you know therefore a great deal about the large, useful, and interesting family to which it and about five thousand other plants belong. The Pea family (also called Pulse or Legume family) is characterized by its "butterfly" flowers and its fruit, which is a legume—a pod that splits into two pieces. The blossom has five irregular petals: An upper one, generally the largest, which is known as the *standard;* two side petals, called *wings;* and two lower ones, joined somewhat to form a sort of pouch, which encloses and protects the sex organs.

Let us start with the Wild Indigos, which are perennial, erect, branching plants with racemes of handsome yellow, cream, blue, and white flowers. Their leaves are like those of clover. It is also called Blue False Indigo. (Above.)

Blue Wild Indigo is up to four feet tall. The violet flowers are in erect round groups up to ten inches long. It grows from southern New Hampshire to Florida, west to Minnesota and south to Texas. It is often cultivated in gardens.

Others with yellow flowers include Catbells (solitary flowers and single leaflets), and Scareweed. White Wild Indigo (tall and smooth) grows in the Midwest.

Yellow Wild Indigo is two or three feet tall. The half-inch flowers are in sparse clusters. The leaves have three short leaflets. It is a welcome plant along roadsides and dry woods west to Minnesota and south to Louisiana.

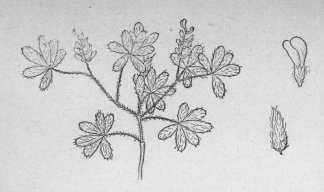

THE LUPINES

Their name derives from the Latin for wolf, but the Lupines are handsome and helpful, for (like other legumes) on their roots live bacteria that fix free nitrogen from the air. They belong to the Pea family. Most of them have lovely blue-purple flowers in terminal groups. They are mostly perennials.

Quakerbonnets (also called Eastern Lupine, Perennial Lupine, and Wild Lupine) is one to two feet tall. Its intensely blue flowers, each two-thirds inch long and sometimes tinged with white or pink, form a sort of spike up to ten inches long. Leaves are divided into eight leaflets arranged (except in number) like the fingers of your hand. The fruit is a hairy pod about two inches long. It grows in dry, sandy hillsides and embankments and open fields sometimes in large colonies, in the east and Midwest. Its extensive roots make it hard to transplant.

Common Bluebonnet and Texas Bluebonnet are almost the same. The first, the Texas state flower, grows only in central and south-central Texas. Both have leaves with five leaflets, blue flowers with a white or purplish spot on the standard, and short racemes. A silky down covers the plants, which are about a foot high. These are among our loveliest flowers.

Low Lupine has many stout branches less than eight inches tall on which are many short racemes. The blue flowers often have a rosy tinge. It is a westerner. It is pictured above.

Other Lupines, which grow westward to the coast and are somewhat described by their names, include Nebraska (bluish gray leaves; dark spot on blue flowers); Silvery Lupine (smaller flowers of purple, violet, rose, or white); Arizona Lupine (white flowers; hairy); western Lupine, and Showy Lupine (dense spikes of sky-blue flowers). That, of course, does not do justice to the Lupines; you will have to experience that pleasure yourself. Nurserymen list fifty species or more in their catalogs.

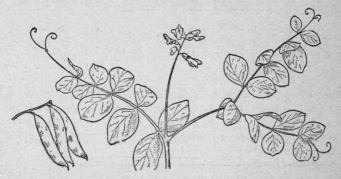

The Beach-pea is a trailing, stout, fleshy vine with tendrils at the tips of its feather-form and rather thick leaves. The purple and violet flowers, each less than an inch long, are in clusters. The pods are veiny and about two inches long. It grows on gravelly slopes and beaches around the Great Lakes and Atlantic coast.

THE CLOVERS

Too well-known, useful, and widespread to need much description are the Clovers, which are of several genera, including *Trifolium* (try-*foh*-lee-um), meaning three-leaved, and have their small "butterfly" flowers massed into dense, round, egg-shaped, or cylindric groups. Their colors are white, yellow, pink, red, and purple. Many of them are valuable forage plants, but several of them can be grown unashamedly for ornament—the handsome Italian Clover for example.

Red Clover: Up to twenty inches high; branchy; hairy;

deep pink flowers; cluster an inch across. Pollinated by bumblebees.

Alsike Clover: Pale pink in a globe-shaped group; smooth stems and leaves; leaflets smaller and broader than Red Clover.

Italian Clover: Bright crimson flowers.

White Clover: Creeping, mat-forming; smooth. White or pale pink flowers.

Rabbit-foot Clover: Off-white tiny flowers that look grayish pink because of the silky tips on the calyx. Narrow, half-inch leaflets.

Hop Clover: Small heads (three-fourths inch) of yellow flowers; to fifteen inches tall; smooth.

Mammoth Clover: Large heads of bright purple.

Tomcat Clover: Light purple, white-tipped, flowers in head more than an inch wide; on west coast.

The Sweet-clovers belong to the genus *Melilotus* and are tall (three to six feet or more) and weedy. They have wiry stems and narrow groups of white and yellow flowers. They are good forage plants.

White Sweet-clover: Branchy; clover-like leaves; fragrant when crushed; many small white flowers in cylindric groups; narrow, short leaflets.

Yellow Sweet-clover: Similar to White-clover; bees like both; it grows almost everywhere.

Here the topic of weeds arose. Why include Sweet-clover Christine asked; they're of little use to anybody.

All plants have a use, I replied. Many provide food for insects, which might become worse pests in food crops if the plants were removed. Some are indicators of soil conditions. Some decorate waste places. Some are the salad and spice of grazing animals. Some protect the ground from erosion that comes from overgrazing, fires, and clearing of land for one reason or another. They are part of the balance of nature. You can add other uses, I am sure.

And so, I continued, what is a weed? No plant need be considered a weed; any plant might be. According to one cliche, a weed is a plant out of place or an unwanted one, no more—a Rose in the Raspberry patch, for example, or a vegetable-garden Dandelion that has invaded the perennial border, or Wild Garlic in a lawn.

SAXIFRAGE AND KIN

Early Saxifrage is known by its cluster of broad and fleshy leaves at the base, and small, fragrant, white flowers grouped at the top of a hairy stem about four inches tall. It likes rocky woodlands as far west as Minnesota. It belongs to the Saxifrage family, which comprises low plants with spikes of small flowers.

The Alumroots, relatives of the Saxifrage, have tufts of toothed, mostly heart-shaped leaves at the base, from which in late spring rise leafless stalks bearing many tiny cup-shaped or saucer-shaped flowers in narrow panicles of white, purple, pink. Most common is the American Alumroot, which has pale pink, yellow, or greenish flowers. It has a thick underground stem and the flower stalk is a foot or two high. It is easy to grow on a slope that is well drained and has somewhat acid soil. Much like it is Midland Alumroot (illustrated above), whose leaf stalks and leaf undersurfaces, however, are notably downy or hairy. Its flowers are only one-third inch long and form a two-valved capsule. It is a native of the Midwest. The others differ in hairiness and the ways the leaves are cut.

Foamflower is like them, but prettier. It has white, small flowers at the tip of a six-inch stalk. Its fuzzy stamens give it its name. You find it in rich woods west to Minnesota and south to Georgia in spring. It is a good ground cover because it is low and spreads into patches.

Miterwort has white, daintily fringed, tiny blossoms in a long, slender group. The flowering stalk is a foot or two high. Its heart-shaped leaves lie on the ground.

77

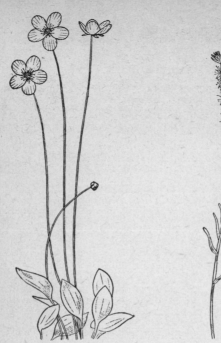

PARNASSIA

Parnassia (or Grass-of-Parnassus) has five clustered leaves at the base, one of which clasps the flower stem. The stem (or scape) is a foot or two tall and bears a one-inch flower. The five petals are rounded and white. The leaves are thick, oval, somewhat heart-shaped. It is sometimes put in the Saxifrage family, whose members it resembles. It likes cool, wet places. (Above left.)

Wild Stonecrop (above, right) is three to six inches tall and has white flowers one-third inch across. The small, pointed leaves are in whorls of three. It inhabits rocky woods and shady banks south to Georgia and west to Michigan. It forms mats that cover the ground and is good to have in the woodland garden.

Among the hundred other kinds of native Sedums is the Spoon Sedum, which is yellow or white.

MEADOW BEAUTY

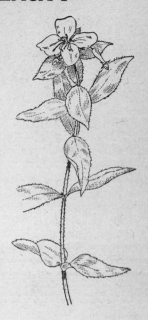

Meadow Beauty is small (up to two feet tall) and has showy flowers with four bright purple or pink petals about an inch across. They fall before noon. It blooms in summer in the East and Midwest in the highly acid soil of damp woods and margins of swamps. The calyx is shaped like an urn with four points. The stamens are conspicuous. The leaves are opposite, somewhat egg-shaped, toothed, and hairy. It is shown to the right. The stems are square and downy. It also bears the names of Handsome Harry and Deer Grass.

This is our only common representative of the large Meadow Beauty family, whose four thousand species are mostly in the Tropics.

Maryland Meadow Beauty is similar, except that it has round stems and is found in sandy swamps in the Northeast, west to Louisiana, and south to Florida.

Other species have white, red, yellow, magenta, and violet-purple blossoms and variations in leaf margins.

As your knowledge of wild flowers increases, so will your use of their scientific names, which are more accurate and interesting that the common ones. A flower might be known by a different name in every part of the country but by only one scientific name the world over. The scientific names are nothing to be afraid of or embarrassed over. A booklet, *The Home Garden Self-Pronouncing Dictionary of Plant Names*, will help you pronounce and define them and tell you about their origin. It is edited by Ralph Bailey.

THE LOOSESTRIFES

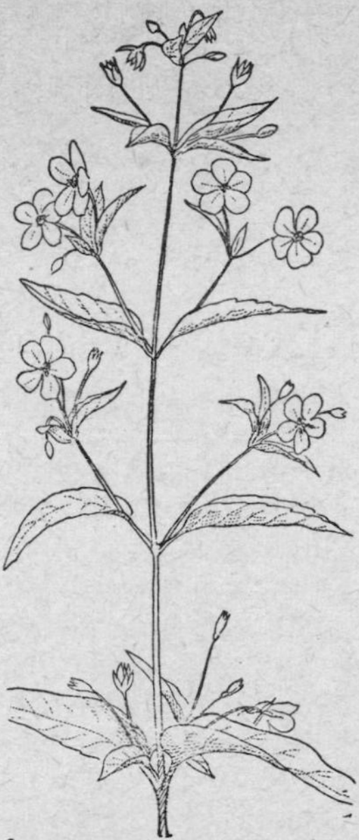

Winged Loosestrife has solitary purple flowers in the axils of the stem leaves. It stands two or three feet high. It blooms in summer in damp thickets as far west as Utah. Southern Loosestrife and Common Loosestrife grow farther south and west.

Showier, coarser, and aggressive to the point of being weedy —although an impressive one!— is the Purple Loosestrife, found widely along streams, swamps, and lakes. Its purple or red-purple flowers make dense, colorful spikes up to five feet high. Often it grows in thick colonies. It is also named Willow Loosestrife.

Those belong to the Loosestrife family (*Lythraceae*—lith-ray-see-ee). Our two dozen species are leaf-stemmed plants with four to six sepals that form a tube, four to six petals, and four to twelve stamens.

In the Primrose family is another group named Loosestrife; they have five to eight petals and five to eight sepals, which are united into a cup. Among them are:

Swamp Candles: About a foot tall; narrow opposite leaves; yellow, purple-striped flowers, each one-third inch wide, in a long group at the apex of the stems. It inhabits marshes in north central states.

Fringed Loosestrife (illustrated above): Hairy stalks two or three feet high; the opposite leaves have white-fringed, hairy stalks. The flowers are in the axils of the leaves and have five pale yellow petals, ragged at the tip. It is found in damp thickets in northern districts.

Lanceleaf Loosestrife: Narrower, lance-shaped leaves; smaller flowers, but more of them.

80

CACTUS

Know the Cacti by the fleshy, enlarged stems that replace
leaves (which would lose too much water in their desert
surroundings), spines that are minute, modified stems,
exquisite flowers of rare beauty, and fleshy, pear-shaped,
edible fruit.

Of our two hundred-odd species, the Prickly-pears are
a group usually distinguished by their jointed and
branching stems.

Western Prickly-pear has flat stem joints and small
brown bristles. It grows in the Midwest and West and
opens in early summer its yellow, red-centered flower. It
prefers open sandy, rocky barrens, and would be an interesting plant for you to try in a sand or rock garden. In
the East and south to Florida is the Eastern Prickly-pear,
in dry, sandy places. It is the only native species in the
Northeast.

Mexican Prickly-pear is fifteen feet high and tree-like.
Its three-inch flowers are orange or yellow. These belong
to the species *Opuntia*—a name you encounter often in
nurserymen's lists.

Of the other Cacti, many might well be mentioned, but
we are content to name two.

Giant Cactus, in southern California and Arizona,
grows to forty feet; each of its four-inch, white waxy flowers blooms but for a night.

Purple Cactus, a picture of which is printed above,
grows from Canada to Kansas and Colorado. It has vivid
purple blossoms.

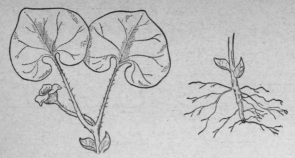

WILD-GINGER

Among the leaves and litter of woods in the eastern half of the country the Wild-Ginger appears in earliest spring—brownish-purple, cup-like, one-inch flowers, shy and almost hidden. From a fleshy, slender underground rootstock, which tastes like ginger, rises the dark-green, hairy, pointed, and kidney-shaped leaves in pairs, three to seven inches across. One plant has only one flower, whose pistil matures first; and to it the gnats and grubs in the forest floor carry pollen from the plants that have flowered earlier. After pollination, the stamens mature, and these fertilize younger flowers. Thus cross-pollinization is assured. The flower has no petals, just three pointed sepals which form the calyx cup.

About a dozen species of Wild-Ginger, all much alike, grow in one part or another of the country.

Another of the 220 species of the Wild-Ginger or Birth-wort family (which all have heart-shaped entire leaves, aromatic sap, and bronzy flowers), is the Pipe-vine. Its flowers have calyx tubes an inch long. They are strangely curved and tipped with a flat, upturned limb that looks indeed like an old-time calabash pipe. Notice also the large, heart-shaped, shiny leaves on stems several inches long. It blossoms in summer from Pennsylvania to Georgia west to Minnesota and Kansas on wooded slopes. It twines as much as thirty feet. It is known also as Dutchman's Pipe for its shape.

Both are easily grown in the garden.

WILLIAM CULLEN BRYANT: *Go forth, under the open sky, and list to Nature's teachings.*

EVENING-PRIMROSE

This is a biennial, two or four feet tall or more, that has erect, coarse stems with many wavy-edge, hairy leaves two to six inches long. The fragrant, yellow flowers, one inch wide and two inches long, open one at a time in late afternoon—evening, that is—or during cloudy days when long-tongued moths, which disseminate the pollen, are up and about. The long sepals end in four distinctive pointed lobes. The plant occurs, sometimes as a weed, in old fields, roadsides, and barren places in the eastern and central areas of the United States. It should be familiar to every country person. Botanists are particularly interested in it, for it is a complex hybrid with many related species and may indicate how rapidly evolution might actually take place.

Other Evening-Primroses—including the Great, Small-flowered, Northern, Oakes, and Prairie Evening-Primrose—differ mostly in size of flower and details of fruit.

Outstandingly brilliant are the Fireweeds, the bright purple giants with which Nature covers a burned forest. They may reach eight feet, and have one-inch flowers in a long, slender group. The seeds have long white hairs.

Pictured here is a close relative, the Purple-leaved Willow-herb, which grows no more than three feet. It has tiny rose-pink flowers nodding at the end of long, slender calyx tubes, which later become seed-pods. The four small petals generally are notched. The leaves are long and narrow. It is widespread in wet ground. It blooms in summer.

THE CARROT FAMILY

Their Latin name *Umbelliferae* ("umbel-bearers") describes the main trait of the Carrots and their kin—celery, parsnips, dill, fennel, and others of the 2,500 species of this large family. The small flowers are in umbels—that is, the stalks of the individual blooms all arise from a single point on a stem and thus form a flattened mass. The fruits are one-seeded and dry.

Queen Anne's Lace, or Wild-Carrot, is a decorative biennial weed one to three feet high. Its flower mass, four inches or less wide, is white, sometimes light pink with a few purple flowers in the middle. The stems are hairy and the leaves are fern-like. It has a fleshy cone of a root. Long ago the garden carrot was developed from it. It is common along roadsides and waste places in summer. In its place it is beautiful, but that place is not fields and pastures. The many varieties differ in small details.

Illustrated is the Rattlesnake Master, a big, bristly perennial of moist plains, with pale-blue flower heads. People used to think it would ward off snakes.

The Golden Alexanders, of which there are several, have yellow flowers in compound umbels. The leaves, on stalks one or two feet high, are twice divided into threes. It is at home in moist meadows in the East. It is easily grown in a wild garden.

Pepper-and-Salt is several inches high. Its flowers have white petals and dark red anthers. It blooms in early spring in the central states on wooded slopes. It supplies early color in the wild garden.

BUNCHBERRY

The Bunchberry, a species of the lovely Dogwood, puts out flowers in a tiny, shy umbel on a flower stalk just a few inches high in May and June. Under the inconspicuous flower cluster are four to six glistening bracts, like large white petals, that give the flower beauty and distinction. A bunch of bright red berries makes the plant handsome in fall and gives it its name. On erect stems three to nine inches high are four to six oval leaves in a whorl. It favors damp woods in rich, highly acid soil from Newfoundland south to Virginia and west to Minnesota.

Another member of the small Dogwood family is the Northern Dwarf Cornel, a lovely thing that has purple flowers and leaves arranged in three to six opposite pairs.

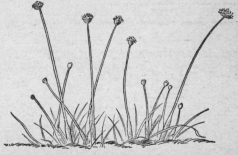

You find the Pipeworts in summer in marshes, swamps, and still water in the eastern two-thirds of the country.

The flowers are tiny, grayish-white, and bunched into heads that look like buttons. The flowers are one-sexed. The leaves are short and in small inch rosettes like grass.

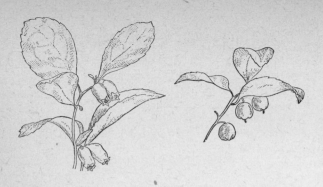

PYROLA

Our twenty-odd species of the Pyrola family are low, smooth, evergreen plants that spread by long slender underground stems. All are of great beauty. Usually the flowers are regular, neatly made, and pink or white.

Round-leaved American-Wintergreen (which you see at the top of this page) has shiny, rounded, thick leathery leaves. The fragrant, nodding, white or pale pink flowers grow in leaf angles on stalks six to twenty inches high —generally longer than the leaves. It likes dry, sandy woods west to Dakota, and flowers in June and July.

Shin Leaf is very much the same. It puts forth its bilateral, nodding, greenish-white flowers, about an inch broad, on a slender, short stalk in July and August as far west as Iowa and New Mexico. The evergreen leaves are thin, basal, oblong, short-stemmed and up to three inches long. Note that the flowers have a protruding style. The plant has a long underground root. It can be grown in an acid woodland garden.

Pipsissewa has white or pink fragrant flowers, less than an inch wide. Two or three of them nod at the tips of the short stalks that rise from the trailing stems. In one species the shining leaves are heavily veined, leathery, and arranged in pairs or triplets. In another kind, the leaves are longer, more pointed, and mottled with white. Green Pipsissewa has solid green, finely toothed leaves. Another name is Prince's Pine. It ranges south to Georgia and southwestward to California. It grows in rich woods.

THE INDIAN PIPES

The Indian Pipes and their fifteen relatives lack chlorophyll with which to make their own food with sunlight. They must depend, therefore, on the soil fungi and decaying humus in the deep woods in which they have their strange and beautiful being. They have no green leaves, but scaly stalks a few inches high. Their family and generic name, *Monotropa,* means one turn— referring, perhaps, to a lonesome plant that turns once toward the light. Another name for them is Corpse Plant.

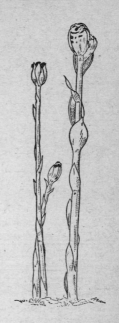

Indian Pipe has white or pale pink stalks (six to ten inches tall) and flowers. The blossoms, which appear in summer through the country, are about three-fourths inch long, and solitary; it nods until it is fertilized, but after that it is upright. The whole plant turns black with age or when it is picked. Do not try to transplant it.

The Pinesaps, of which there are several subspecies, have several nodding (later erect) buff to red flowers in a one-sided raceme on hairy stalks of the same tint. The topmost flower has five parts; often the others have three or four parts. They bloom in summer and fall in woods where there is humus of moderate acidity.

Of the same affinity are the Pigmypipes, less than five inches high, scaly, not hairy, and pink, purple, white, and brown in color. They grow from Maryland southward.

Much larger are the Pinedrops. They grow to four feet and at the top have racemes of many white flowers. The brownish stems are hairy and sticky. It is found in pine woods south to Pennsylvania and westward.

TRAILING-ARBUTUS

Few flowers can equal in beauty the Trailing-Arbutus, which enlivens the drabness of late winter on wooded slopes and sandy flats, often under evergreens, in the eastern half of North America. The fragrant, white-pink flowers are a tube two-thirds of an inch long. The plant is a low-growing undershrub. It is hard to transplant to one's own wild garden—the seeds are minute; one cannot pick the flowers without uprooting part of the plant; and the plant is sensitive to changes (such as caused by fire and lumbering) in its habitat. It is disappearing from many areas.

Trailing-Arbutus is one of the thousand species of the Heath family, along with trees and shrubs like Azalea, Rosebay, Laurel, Leatherleaf, Heather, Blueberry, and Cranberry. Among them also is Wintergreen and Galax. It is pictured above.

Creeping Wintergreen has slender, creeping stems that send up low shoots. The solitary flowers have five white petals that form an urn-shaped tube. The leaves are evergreen. The berries are fleshy and red. The plant has the wintergreen fragrance. It lives in woods and bogs in the Northeast and blooms in summer.

Rare and limited to the Blue Ridge area are the Galax (which has many small white flowers on a leafless stalk about fifteen inches tall, and shiny, leather leaves) and Oconee Bells, a lovely evergreen plant with oval leaves and a solitary, nodding, white bell-shaped flower and a single flower stalk six inches high. Both are somewhat hard to grow, but you might try them in your wild garden.

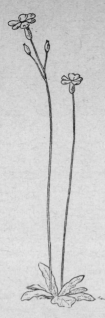

THE
PRIMROSES

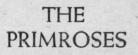

Primroses, or Primula, are northern plants, famed in song and story. If you know the beautiful garden sorts, you can easily tell the wild ones. They all have single flower stalks up to eighteen inches high and bearing a cluster of bright, star-shaped, symmetrical flowers. Many have a vivid yellow or orange spot, known as an eye, in the center. They like damp, cool places, sometimes rocky cliffs. About two dozen grow in the United States from Maine west to Minnesota and in high western mountains. Most of them have lilac, purple, or blue flowers. Above, left, is Dwarf Canadian Primrose.

Their name tells a lot about twenty kinds of Shooting Stars: The five petals and five sepals point upward and their five long lobes are bent backward. The stamens form a cone, so that the inch-long flower looks like a dart.

Midland Shooting Star has deep pink to white flowers in an umbel on a stalk about a foot tall. It blossoms in late spring in the central states in open woods and meadows. (Above, right.)

Tall Bell Flower
(Page 115)

Sneezeweed
(Page 125)

Ironweed (Page 121)

THE GENTIANS

If you are lucky enough to find a bright blue flower about eighteen inches high, rather tube-like, and so lovely that you want to write a poem about it, you very likely have a Gentian, one of the handsomest of all flowers. Do not pick it; enjoy it where it is. Most Gentians prefer damp thickets and grasslands. Of our hundred species, it is hard to select just a few to discuss, but the outstanding ones include:

Fringed Gentian, one of America's best-loved flowers, grows west to Minnesota and Iowa and south to Georgia. Its two-inch flowers, borne a dozen or so on a stem, are on long stalks, whose rather broad leaves almost parallel the stem. The four unequal sepals and four petals unite to form a trumpet or bell, whose equal, rounded lobes at the apex are fringed. On dull days the flowers close to protect nectar and organs, but on sunny autumn days the flowers open out. It is biennial.

Smaller Fringed Gentian has a wider range, smaller size, linear instead of lance-shaped leaves, and one to six flowers on a plant. It is annual.

Yellow Midland Gentian is a perennial less than two feet high. It has pale yellow, bell-shaped flowers.

Narrow-leaf Gentian has light-blue petals with a greenish tip. The flower is a narrow funnel, not spreading.

Short-leaf Midland Gentian is about a foot high.

Bottle Gentian is about eighteen inches high. The dark violet-blue flowers, an inch and a half long, are club-shaped and in clusters in the upper leaf axils.

DOGBANE

Dogbane has a milky, bitter sap that keeps grazing animals away but lures certain butterflies, which, in turn, can secrete a similar bitter substance for protection against their enemies. Rosy Dogbane, above, averages two feet in height and has little clusters of pink, nodding b e l l flowers. Other sorts have white, blue, or purple flowers. They are found in early summer west to the Rockies. Pink-flowered Spreading Dogbane is shrubby.

Buckbean

Related to the Gentians are the thirty-some kinds of Buckbeans (shown at the left). Three-leaf Buckbean—or Bogbean— has thick, low stems which creep in bogs. The flowers, less than a half inch wide, form a cylinder-spike at the top of a six-inch stalk. The white petals have shiny hairs. The leaves look like Bean leaves. It grows in cool, northern places.

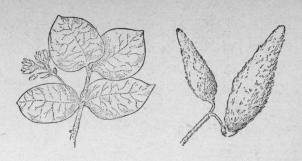

THE MILKWEEDS

As you already know, the Milkweeds have milky juice, characteristic umbels of many small flowers that range from dull pink to orange red, and peculiar, boat-shaped pods that contain seeds tufted with floss, which is lighter than cork and warmer than wool.

Butterflyweed, brightest and least weedy of all, is about a foot high and is bright orange yellow, with greenish corollas. The leafy, upright stems are covered with coarse hairs. The leaves, about four inches long, are oblong, nearly stalkless, and arranged alternately on the stems. The pods are four inches long and downy. A perennial, it blooms in summer in dry fields and sandy slopes.

Common Milkweed, your friend of field and roadside, grows to five feet in rich ground. It has thick, hairy, stems and blunt, oval leaves about six inches long. The large, drooping umbels of flowers vary from pink to green-brown-yellow. Above the corolla is a crown of hoods about a fourth inch broad.

Showy Milkweed, which is much like it but grows farther west, is illustrated.

Swamp Milkweed, whose dull pink flowers are half as large as those of the Common Milkweed, also ranges widely. It grows to four feet.

Purple Milkweed has magenta flowers, four-inch pods, three-foot stems, and thick leaves. The stem is slender. It likes dry fields.

Four-leaf Milkweed is only two feet high. Its pale pink flowers are in several small umbels. The slender pods are four inches long. The lower stalk has few or no leaves.

93

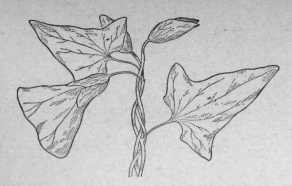

MORNING GLORY

Anyone who knows the glorious Heavenly Blue **Morning Glory** or another of the newly developed garden *Ipomoea* (eye-poh-*mee*-ah, meaning twisting or worm-like) hardly needs an introduction to their wild but no less attractive country cousins. All have rather large flowers of glistening white or bright colors, whose five petals are completely united into a funnel-shaped corolla. The family name Convolvulus means rolling-around.

Hedge Bindweed (Wild Morning Glory) has twining or climbing stems up to ten feet long and deep, persistent roots, the bane of farmers and gardeners. But west as far as Texas all summer it makes a profusion of two-inch funnel flowers, white or light pink with lighter stripes or purple throat. The leaves are large, smooth, and triangular or heart-shaped. If you want to color the drawing of it on this page, you can let your imagination go.

American Bindweed is like it. Usually it has rose-purple flowers, beautiful ones, and grows along fence-rows west to New Mexico.

Upright Bindweed, white, has a low stalk that twines only at the tip.

Field Bindweed, pink or white, has small, arrow-shaped leaves, stems only about two feet long, and bell-shaped flowers. It covers waysides the country over.

Big-root Morning Glory has an enormous, fleshy root that weighs up to twenty-five pounds. The funnel flowers are two or three inches long, white or pink or pale purple.

JACOB'S LADDER

These belong to the Phlox family and usually are lavender-purple and tubular or bell-shaped. All of the dozen species are handsome.

Greek-valerian has smooth, slender stems a foot high, which bear pinnate and half-inch, locust-like leaves and violet flowers in their axils. The five unequal, prominent white stamens provide the other color of the blue and white Greek flag. It blooms in spring in open woods and meadows as far west as Kansas and Minnesota and south to Georgia. It is a good plant for the wild garden.

American Jacob's Ladder, which you see above, has straighter stems, larger, darker flowers, and lives in Northeastern bogs. It is perennial and grows to three feet from a horizontal root. The flowers are little less than an inch across, clustered at the top of the stems, bell-shaped, and blue purple. The leaflets, three to twenty to a leaf, are cut feather-like—pinnate, that is. This is another attractive plant that needs your protection. Sometimes it is known simply as Jacob's Ladder—the leaves are the clue.

Western Jacob's Ladder has deep blue bells. It blooms in summer westward from Dakota.

Leafy Jacob's Ladder, a Southwesterner, has more flowers, bigger leaves, and leafier stems.

Several species with yellow, pink, and cream flowers are found along the west coast.

Swamp Valerian, found west to the Rockies, has tiny pink-white-magenta flowers in loose clusters.

PHLOX

Our half-hundred kinds of Phlox are all small plants with showy flowers, whose five sepals and five petals are united at the base and flaring at the top to form a trumpet with a star-shaped limb. Garden Phlox are among our brightest flowers; the wild ones tend to be of more subdued pink to deep lavender. Often they have an eye—an arresting spot of color at the throat.

Woodland Phlox is outstanding, as you see from the drawing. It is about a foot tall. Its open, fragrant, tubular, trumpet-shaped flowers are light violet. The five petals are slightly notched at the tip. It blooms in spring over most of the eastern half of the country west to Minnesota and Eastern Oklahoma in woods and meadows. It is also named Wild Blue Phlox and Wild Sweet William.

Meadow Phlox is two or three feet high. Its purple to white flowers are in a looser, more cylindric group. The leaves are opposite and smaller and often streaked with purple. It is found in wet thickets and meadows from Connecticut to Missouri.

Downy Phlox is covered with hairs. The flowers, in late spring, are white, pink, or purple.

Moss Phlox has low, moss-like tufts, needle-like leaves that often are evergreen, and half-inch white or purple flowers, which often have a purple eye. Often found in gardens as *Phlox sublata*, it is native in uplands from North Carolina to Michigan.

WATERLEAF

A relative of the Phlox is the Waterleaf family, whose two hundred species include delicate plants with large, long-stalked, feather-shaped leaves. The five sepals and five petals (which often are of a blue-lavender color) are more or less united into a tube. The flowers are clustered on weak stems a foot or two high.

Virginia Waterleaf is downy. You see it above. The third inch blossoms, in clusters, have narrow, spreading sepals and white to violet petals. Filaments of the stamens are hairy. The leaves have five or seven pointed segments. They look as if stained with water, a detail that both common and scientific names *(Hydrophyllum)* recognize.

Large-leaf Waterleaf is hairier and has blunter leaflets and white flowers. It is found in woods in summer.

Lavender Waterleaf, also a foot or two high and hairy, has half-inch, funnel-shaped flowers of lavender blue. It is a spring flower in the Midwest.

Miami-mist or Pursh Phacelia have finely fringed, wheel-shaped flowers that shade from white at the base to blue at the outside. The leaves are deeply lobed and about two inches long. It lives in open fields in the central states, where it can become a weed, albeit a beautiful one.

Fern-leaf Phacelia has lavender flowers in a loose spiral. It grows about two feet tall and has coarse down. The flowers are funnel-shaped and have fringes at the base. The divided leaves are fern-like. It blooms in early summer in midwestern woods.

BLUEBELLS

Christine asked me to devote an extra page to our favorite flower, Virginia Bluebell. Two solid colonies of it grow in stream-bordered pastures near our home. They put a blue blanket down among the trees in April; a month or so later flower and foliage disappear, leaving a memory, exciting and clear, that remains until the next display is put on. We make a pilgrimage to them each spring.

Bluebells belong to the Borage family and the genus *Mertensia*. They are about a foot high. The specific name is *virginica;* Virginia has given its name to nothing more entrancing than this perennial. The pink-budded, blue flowers appear in early spring. Then the gray-green foliage dies as the seeds mature, several weeks later. The trumpet-shaped flowers are an inch long and in loose clusters—curled-up racemes and in the upper axils. The smooth leaves are large and oval, untoothed and bluntly pointed. It is also called (for the record) Virginia Cowslip and Tree Lungwort, but Cowslip could be better used for Primula or Primrose, and Lungwort, as far as we are concerned, can stay in the books. You can easily grow it in your wild garden or any place that has rich, neutral, rather moist soil.

Lanceleaf Mertensia is the western form. It has half-inch, funnel flowers and willowy leaves. It grows in thickets west of the Great Plains.

In the North one finds Tall Mertensia (or Tall Lungwort), which grows to three feet and has sparse groups of reddish-blue flowers. The plant is rough and hairy.

FORGET-ME-NOT,
HELIOTROPE, PUCCOON

The Forget-me-Nots (above, left) are small, light blue or white flowers with a yellow center—charming plants that bring to mind the garden varieties. There are ten kinds, all with tiny blossoms.

Heliotrope are showy flowers of limited range, but of many colors—yellow, white, blue, rose, purple. Indian Heliotrope grows three feet tall, has blue flowers, and has adapted itself to fields and roadsides through the South. (Above, middle.)

Puccoon (above, right) is known for its deep root, downy leaves, and clusters of yellow, trumpet-shaped flowers. Narrowleaf Puccoon is about two feet high and grows in the middle West and south to Texas.

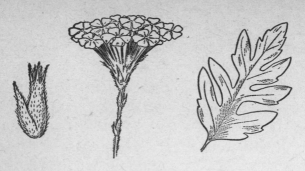

VERBENA

The Verbenas, or Vervains, have small flowers that often are a showy lavender-purple trumpet—that is, the sepals are united into a tube and petals are joined below but flare into a flat dish at the top. Mostly the leaves are coarsely toothed and opposite in pairs. We have about two hundred of the world's three thousand species, which include the Teak tree and Lemon Verbena.

Midland Vervain has many branches about a foot tall. The half-inch flowers, usually a dull purple but some times white through rose, form a dense cluster. It grows in the eastern two-thirds of America in dry thickets and pastures and blooms in summer. It is a good plant for a rock garden in ordinary soil.

Blue Vervain is four or five feet tall and has a compound group of small, slender violet-blue spikes. The leaves are large, pointed, and roughly toothed and in whorls of five. Look for it in moist places and waste places in summer almost everywhere.

Small-flowered Verbena has flowers that range from pink to purple on hairy branches about fifteen inches high. The leaves are finely cut. It is often found in large colonies from the Mississippi westward.

Pictured above is Canada Verbena, whose large, blue-purple flowers appear in dry soil in May to August.

Among the Verbenas farther west are the Western Pink Verbena (blue-purple or pink), Southwestern (downy), Showy White (white), and Moss Verbena (blue, prostrate branches).

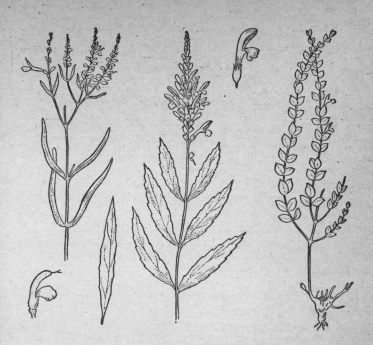

SAGE, DRAGONHEAD,
SKULLCAP

The Purple Sage, with or without riders, has more romance but less beauty than the two or three dozen other Sages, or Salvias. Tall Sage, the tallest, is five feet high (above, left). Its blue flowers are in long, thick spikes set off by gray-green foliage. It grows in the dry plains.

Dragonheads (above, middle) have inch-long, pink-purple flowers in thick groups on sturdy stems three feet high. The leaves are shiny, stiff, toothed ribbons. They inhabit low ground south and west of Pennsylvania.

The name of the blue-violet Skullcaps comes from their peculiar calyx, which has two lips. The upper of two sepals bears a hump like a skullcap; the lower one bends downward. It is pictured above, right. Showy Skullcap, which grows in woodlands in the central states, has inch-long flowers in clusters above the leaves.

BERGAMOT

There are three thousand species of Mint, about which you know a great deal already if you have at least a smelling acquaintance with Peppermint, Spearmint, Rosemary, Sage, Thyme, Marjoram, Lavender, or Bergamot. They have (1) aromatic oils, (2) square stems, and (3) opposite, rather leathery, leaves. Note well those three key marks. The bilateral flowers are in cymes or spikes; petals, sepals, stamens, and pistils are in fours or fives. Vervains and Mints are closely related.

First the Bergamots, of the genus *Monarda* (mon-*ar*-duh) which are the handsomest.

Scarlet Wild Bergamot is two or four feet high. Its bright red flowers, each about an inch and a half long and with petals united to form two lips, are borne in dense but rather ragged cluster. Under the flower heads are leaf-like bracts that also are red. The broad, thin leaves have coarse teeth and a pleasant scent when you crush them. It likes moist woods and roadsides and old-fashioned gardens west to Michigan and south to Georgia, and it puts on its show in summer. Other names: Oswego Tea and Beebalm. Hummingbirds go for it, as they do many red flowers.

Wild Bergamot is like it, except that its flower is a little shorter, it is usually dull lavender or lilac (but sometimes pinkish), and it grows in drier places over a wider range. Another name is Lavender Bergamot. Its picture is printed at the top of this page.

Spotted Wild Bergamot (Common Horsemint) has yellow flowers with purple spots about an inch long.

The upper leaves and bracts are pink, white, or brown-purple to add to the colorfulness. The flower heads appear at the apex of the many branches and in the axils. It blooms from July to October in wastelands and open dry woods from New York to Florida, west to Minnesota and south to Texas. The foliage smells like Thyme.

OTHER WILD MINTS

All these, remember, have square stems and small flowers that range from purplish-red through white and are borne in spikes or heads. They are fragrant. They tend to become a little too friendly.

American Mint: One foot high; forms clumps by underground stems; tiny, pale lavender or light purple flowers in clusters in axils of leaves; late summer; moist places.

Gill-over-the-Ground: Pale blue, two-lipped corolla; rounded leaves; widespread in damp places; mostly low.

Common Dittany (Stonemint) : Wiry, reddish stems, about a foot high; small pink-lavender flowers in bunches; dry hills in East; leaves egg-shaped and toothed.

Catnip: Two or three feet high; downy, branching stems; small whitish-pink-lavender flowers in interrupted spikes at the ends of branches; damp places.

Wild Marjoram: Hairy, two-foot stems two-lipped purplish flowers in a spike with purplish bracts; along roadsides; June to October.

Motherwort: Stout, erect, five-foot stems; small, lilac flowers; lower leaves have irregular lobes, upper leaves are wedge-shaped.

Pennyroyal: Foot high; branches have fine hairs; the small, two-lipped flowers are light purple; dry ground.

Self-heal (Heal-all) : Foot or two tall; tiny lilac flowers in spike about an inch long, longer after flowers die; leaves bright green or purplish; everywhere.

Blue Curls: Up to eighteen inches tall; small blue flowers on long stalks, first at the end and then in the leaf axils; four long, curving stamens protrude; leaves lance-shaped, covered with smelly wax; autumn in shady places.

NIGHTSHADE

The Petunia, which everyone knows, is a good example of the Potato, or Nightshade, family. It is a large clan that embraces the Tomato, Potato, Sweet Peppers, Belladonna, Eggplant, Groundcherry, and nearly two thousand other economic and ornamental plants.

The key to the flowers is the star-shaped or wheel-shaped corolla, the five sepals and five petals being united. The flowers often are an attractive white, yellow, blue, or purple. The fruit frequently is a showy berry.

Easy to spot is the Horse Nettle, a prickly plant one to two feet high. The one-inch flowers are white or lilac and star- or wheel-shaped. They produce an orange-yellow berry. The leaves have coarse lobes. It blooms in summer in the eastern half of the country in thickets, grasslands, and waste places. Farmers abhor it.

Botanists have trouble in classifying members of the genus *Solanum* (so-*lay*-num), but one key will help you: The five, long, bright yellow anthers form a narrow cone protruding conspicuously from the center of the flower.

Bitter-Sweet (or sometimes simply Nightshade, which is illustrated above) is a climbing perennial about eight feet long. The flowers are half-inch purple cones with yellow centers and in groups. The stamens stick out prominently from the flower. The leaves are about three inches long, often lobed at the base or with two projections that resemble ears. (Deadly Nightshade is entirely different, but we need not bother with it.) Bitter-Sweet has red oval berries in drooping clusters.

TOADFLAX

Another large family (three thousand species) is the Snapdragon or Figwort relationship, of which the best known is the Snapdragon of greenhouse and garden. If

you take it with you in your mind's eye, it will help you make a pretty good guess at the identity of scores of flowers. They all have the same strange spur in the corolla.

Like a small yellow and orange Snapdragon is the Yellow Toadflax, which you might know better as Butter and Eggs. It grows one to three feet high and has many narrow, smooth, blue-green leaves scattered over the generally unbranched stalk. The corolla is two-lipped; its base becomes a long yellow spur. The upright upper lip has two lobes; the lower lip has three spreading lobes and forms a "palate" that is bright orange. It blossoms almost everywhere in June to October.

It came from Europe; to some it is just a weed.

Blue Toadflax is two feet high or less. Its small lavender-blue flowers are in a long slender group. There is a white palate and a small spur. It appears in summer over much of the United States in sandy places. It has linear leaves like Yellow Toadflax, but the flowers are much smaller. Both belong to the genus *Linaria,* from *linum,* flax.

Texas Toadflax has larger blue and white flowers.

Star Toadflax, pictured at the top, is like the preceding only in name. A member of the Sandalwood family, it is a foot-high weed with small greenish white flowers, whose calyx has five starry lobes and a cup, no spur.

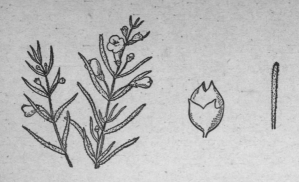

GERARDIA; TURTLE HEAD

Gerardia is erect, branching, rose-purple, and bell-shaped. It is partly parasitic and turns black when dry. The flowers, two-thirds inch long, occur in the axils of bracts. Two petals form a short upper lip; the other three make a spreading lower lip. Leaves are narrow and opposite.

Chelone (kee-*low*-nee, which means tortoise) resembles the head of a turtle or snake. The flowers have two lips and are somewhat hooded; the lower lip has a hairy palate. White Turtle Head is two or three feet high and has a dense spike of inch-long white flowers with a purple tip. One of the four stamens is short and useless. The leaves are sharply toothed and about two inches long. It grows in wet places in the East and blooms in fall.

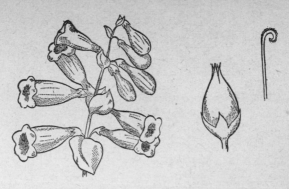

BEARD TONGUE

Called so because one of the five stamens is like a tongue a child sticks out and is tipped with a beardlike bunch of hairs, the Beard Tongues are unusual—and among the handsomest of Snapdragons.

The two hundred-odd species grow in all parts in light woods, grasslands, and sandy slopes, and their flowers are of many colors—scarlet, blue, purple, white, yellow. Another name for them is *Penstemon* (pen-*stee*-mun), which refers to the five white stamens, of which four only can perform the male function of producing pollen.

Eastern Beard Tongue has one-inch, violet-purple blooms that form a funnel or tube and are flattened and lighter-colored at the tip. The flowers are loosely clustered on the stalk. It is about two feet high and grows in eastern states in dry ground. The leaves have shallow notches and are about three inches long.

Crested Beard Tongue has red-purple flowers in narrow panicles at the tips of stems. It lives in the Midwest.

Large-flowered Beard Tongue grows to three feet, also in the Prairie states. Its flowers are creamy or pinkish.

Smooth White Beard Tongue is most common in the East. Its many flowers are in a compound group—little over an inch long, white with purple lines, and spreading outward to a trumpet shape. The leaves are large and toothed. It inhabits grasslands and woods margins in the Midwest, but it extends eastward.

Under suitable conditions, they are good garden plants.

MONKEY FLOWER

These are showy plants of swamps and wet meadows. Their large, double-lipped, tubular, short-stalked flowers are in the upper leaf axils. Their name comes from the vague suggestion of a monkey face in the way two petals make an upper lip and the other three a lower lip. *Mimulus,* the genus name, means "little mimic."

Square-Stemmed Monkey Flower has smooth, four-angled stems two to three feet tall. The flowers are violet-purple and an inch long, and have a cylindrical tube which is longer than the calyx. It flowers from June to September south to Virginia and west to Texas. Its pointed, lance-shaped leaves are sessile and the flowers have long stalks.

Wing-stem Monkey Flower has inch-long lavender flowers. Flowers and leaves are short-stalked. The leaves are coarsely toothed. It blooms in summer in the South. It is depicted above.

Musk Monkey Flower has smaller yellow flowers. The leaves and stems are hairy and sticky. The leaves are not deeply indented. The corolla is somewhat flat. It has a musky odor. It is native to the West, but it is found elsewhere as a fugitive from gardens. It can be grown on the banks of a stream or pond.

Tobacco Monkey Flower, in California, has red flowers.

There are about forty kinds of Monkey Flower, some of them horticultural varieties that you see in greenhouses and florists' shops.

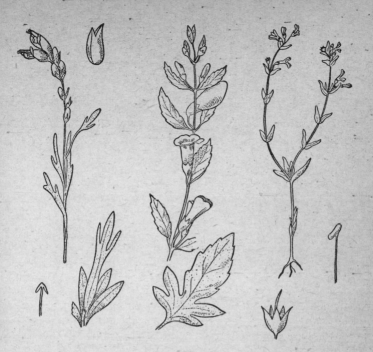

OTHER SNAPDRAGONS

Bright as brilliant paint are the Painted Cups, or Indian Paintbrushes (above, left). The flowers usually are nondescript green-yellow and small, but the color comes from the gay, fanlike, leaflike bracts beneath them. There are two-score varieties. The Scarlet Painted Cup is one or two feet tall. The leaves are arranged alternately on straight stems; the top ones are bright red or scarlet. It grows in grassy thickets from New England to Minnesota south to Texas, and is a partial parasite of other green plants.

Near Oak trees, whose sap they suck, live the ten species of False-Foxgloves, yellow, funnel-form flowers of some beauty (above, middle). They are also called Oak Leech. Lace-leaf False-Foxglove is about three feet tall and covered with sticky, hairy, and lacy leaves. Many bronzy, yellow flowers are borne in loose clusters, each a little more than an inch long and an inch wide at the end.

Common almost everywhere in moist thickets and meadows in summer is Culvers-root, a three- to five-foot plant. Its unbranched stem carries several round, dense spikes of tiny white flowers. The central spike may be three to nine inches long; the others are shorter. The sepals are united into a tube, beyond which two stamens extend. Leaves grow in whorls of four to eight and are long and pointed. It is suitable for a wild garden. (Above, left.)

The Wood Betony is another of the Snapdragons. It is a foot or less tall. Its yellow flowers, sometimes of a reddish tinge, grow in thick spikes or heads up to six inches long. The corolla has two lips, the upper one of which has a hood. The leaves are fern-like. It grows in woods and moist grasslands in eastern areas. (Above, right.)

A rather rare member of the Snapdragon family is Blue-eyed Mary (page 109, right), a delicate plant six to eighteen inches high. Three blue-lavender petals unite to form a lower lip and two white ones make an upper lip.

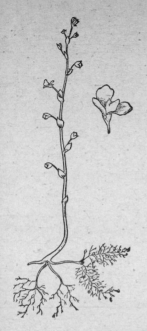
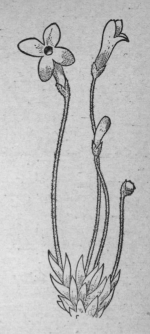

BLADDERWORT

The twenty kinds of Bladderwort have small, bilateral flowers, tiny roots, and small leaves or none at all, but they are highly interesting aquatic or bog plants because they trap their food. Among the leaves and roots are small, green, round bladders, each with a small opening and a bristly flap that opens and shuts and captures small worms, larvae, and such. Cells inside digest the animal matter. They are among our smallest flowering plants.

Purple Bladderwort has lavender-purple flowers on stalks that stand about four inches above the surface of the water. It blooms in summer. It has a thick, blunt spur.

Lake Bladderwort, a more common sort, has somewhat larger yellow flowers. Its picture is above, left. Beneath the surface of the pond its roots make thick masses. It ranges widely over North America, but you have to look carefully for it, because the flower is just above the surface on a delicate stalk.

SOME PARASITES

Plants that steal their living are called parasites. Most plants struggle to expose the largest possible leaf surface to the sun so as to make all their food, but parasites need no green coloring matter—chlorophyll—or real leaves because they send their roots into another plant and feed on its sap.

Among the parasites are several members of the Broom-rape family, whose flowers resemble those of the Bladder-worts and Snapdragons in having two-lipped, tubular flowers, although the fruits are different.

Squaw Root is a fleshy mass a few inches high, and covered with stiff, light brown, overlapping scales. Many small yellowish flowers, each with two bracts underneath, form a dense spike about an inch thick. The stamens extend from the flower. It blooms in May to August south to Florida and west to Michigan in rich woods (mostly Oak). It takes nourishment from the tree roots.

Ghost Pipe (shown on page 111) also has scaly stems that make a dense mat in forest litter and among roots of various plants. The stalks, about five inches tall, bear two-lipped, lavender flowers one-half inch long. The calyx is shaped like a bell and is hairy. It blooms May to July west to Texas.

Beechdrops have erect, slender stiff stems that are yellow-brown and up to twenty inches high. The upper flowers are mostly sterile. The calyx is short and five-toothed. The lower flowers are small and closed. The fruit is a tiny capsule. It is parasitic on the roots of Beech.

Among other parasitics are Mistletoe, which engrafts itself on branches of Hickory, Oak, and other trees, and the well-known Dodder, which has orange or white, thread-like stems and white bell-shaped flowers.

Another group of dependent plants, to which we have been introduced, are saprophytes, which get all their nourishment from humus and decaying vegetable matter, not from living plants. Among them is Indian Pipe.

Epiphytes are "air-plants"—Spanish Moss, Wild Pine, many Orchids, and others. Their roots do not touch the ground.

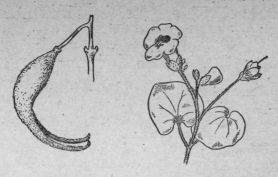

UNICORN; RUELLIA

This strange plant is outstanding because of its pesky, sometimes dangerous, fruit. It is an elastic capsule, four or six inches long and shaped like the letter U. When it is ripe and brittle, it breaks off easily, and a claw-like beak fastens to the leg of a passing animal, which thus disseminates the many seeds within. Should it get into the nose of grazing animals, the sharp hooks might cause infection. It has sprawling stems and hairy, clammy leaves. The bronzy pink, spotted, and rather attractive flowers are less than two inches across and of a funnel shape.

Another small family embraces ten species of Ruellia (or "Wild-Petunia"), which have attractive, blue-purple, funnel-shaped flowers. Smooth Ruellia (shown above) has blue flowers two inches long and erect stems one to three feet high. Night-blooming Ruellia has four-inch, pale blue flowers, and lives in the far South.

THE BLUETS

Charming, small, blue or lavender flowers are these members of the Madder family, whose six thousand species (of which we have about a hundred) include Coffee, Ipecac, and other medicinal and dye plants. Distinguishing marks of the group are whorled or opposite leaves and petals and sepals usually in fours.

Common Bluets (which you surely know) in early spring carpet acres of old pastures and fields with blue. Their small, trumpet flowers, yellow-centered, appear singly on wiry stalks six inches high or less. The small, spoon-shaped leaves are placed opposite to each other in basal rosettes and form tufts. Other names for them are Wild Forget-me-Nots, Quaker Ladies, Quaker Bonnets, and Angel Eyes—in token, I think, of the wide range and wide esteem.

Fringed Summer Bluets are a little taller. The lilac flowers are in groups of two or three and in the axils of bracts at the tips of the branches. The petals are united to form a longer funnel or trumpet. Look for it on open banks in the central states.

Least Bluets are less than three inches tall. They also make lavender blankets over Midwest hillsides in April.

Relatives of the Bluets are the Bedstraws, which are marked by tiny white flowers and leaves in whorls of four (Small Bedstraw), five or six (Rough Bedstraw), or six to eight (Cleaver Bedstraw). Rough Bedstraw, the handsomest, has spreading branches and airy groups of four-parted flowers. It grows in damp ground. The plants were used to stuff mattresses—hence the name.

THE BELL FLOWERS

The Bluebells of Scotland grow not only in Scotland but in many parts of the world. They are delicate plants, but as rugged as a Scotsman and, in their way, as canny. For one thing, they show differences in growth and looks to conform to their habitat; also, in their evolution, their five petals, once separate, became more and more united into a bell. Such a form insures that all the pollen is held in the cup; insects that visit it have to touch the stigmas. Also, no pollen is wasted; if all else fails, the stigmas droop in order to shed pollen on the plant's own ovaries. The Bell Flower (Campanula) family is set apart by delicacy of its plants, milky juice, and the radial flowers.

Bluebells are deep blue, bell-shaped, and nodding on thin stalks up to eighteen inches high. The lower leaves are rounded, but the upper ones are ribbon-like. It blooms in summer over the Northern states on sandy hillsides. It is named also Scotch Bluebell or Harebell, or Varied-leaf Bluebell. Do not confuse it with Virginia Bluebell (see page 98), which is shorter, has trumpet-shaped flowers and wider leaves, and is all in all a stouter, leafier plant. The two have nothing in common except name. The two illustrate a reason why, if you carry your flower studies further, you should learn (or at least note) the scientific names. They are distinctive, descriptive, and not difficult once you see the system they follow.

Eastern Harebell, which grows from Pennsylvania to Iowa, combines thin stem leaves and heart-shaped lower leaves and thin stems, the better to withstand winds. The blue flowers are sparse and hanging downward on delicate stalks. It likes shady banks.

Western Harebell, in the far West, has thicker leaves.

Tall Bell Flower, pictured on page 90, has thin stems two to six feet high and dull blue to white flowers of a wheel (not bell) shape in one-foot spikes. It blooms in summer over the eastern half of the country.

Star Bell Flower is about three feet high and has deep blue flowers an inch across. Leaves are toothed and narrow. It lives in rocky woods in the East.

THE LOBELIAS

Harold N. Moldenke, curator of the New York Botanical Garden and author of the excellent book, *American Wild Flowers,* conducted a poll of American naturalists to a s c e r t a i n their opinion on the showiest, most conspicuous, and most interesting wild plants. The leader turned out to be the Cardinal Flower. With reason: The Cardinal Flower (or Red Lobelia) brings fiery beauty to swamps, wet meadows, ditches, and low ground generally westward to Colorado in late summer. Its inch-and-a-half flowers appear in the axils of small bracts and make noble terminal racemes. The calyx has a short, five-cleft tube; the corolla has two lips, one of them split. The stamens stand away from the corolla. The plant itself is two to four feet  high. The leaves are oval or oblong, sharply pointed, and sometimes of a bronzy sheen. Truly a lovely creation, made lovelier still by hummingbirds, which like the red flowers.

Great Blue Lobelia, another of the six hundred species of the Lobelia family, is like it, but it grows only up to two feet or so and its blue flowers are an inch long. Like the other, its leaves are less than five inches long, pointed, and slightly serrated. Both are well worth planting in the moist wild garden.

Indian Tobacco has smaller flowers and an inflated pod. Also, the leaves are egg-shaped and sparingly toothed.

Lime Lobelia is a slender, branching plant less than a foot tall. It has small, lavender-blue flowers on long stalks. The narrow leaves have tiny teeth.

CHICORY

Dandelions, Lettuce, Oyster Plant, Hawkweeds, Chicory, and a thousand other species are grouped in the Chicory family because of several mutual characteristics: Milky juice; alternate leaves; minute flowers packed together into a tight head, which itself is often mistaken for one flower; and the habit of opening for a day, closing, and then reopening when the fruits are mature. Another distinguishing mark is that the five stamens are united into a tube at the bottom and to "straps" at the top.

Common Chicory is a many-branched perennial two or three feet tall. The flower heads are an inch or so across and have many rays of blue, sometimes white. Its leaves are narrow and have wavy margins. Sometimes it is called Coffeeweed because its long taproot is ground and added to coffee. It blooms summerlong almost everywhere.

Goat-Dandelion has bright orange rays and heads about an inch and a half wide on stalks that are about a foot high. The leaves are smooth and gray-green. It blossoms in early summer as far west as Colorado. Carolina Dwarf Dandelion is similar but smaller.

Common Dandelion, or just plain Dandelion, is one of our most beautiful flowers, one of the gayest, one of the earliest, one of the most welcome, and, unfortunately, one of the most persistent in places where it is not wanted. The velvety flower heads, sometimes two inches wide, contain about a hundred yellow-rayed florets. The leaves are irregularly toothed and lobed and are several inches long. This Dandelion came from Europe, but we have a half dozen natives that are almost alike.

THE COMPOSITES

If you call a flower you do not know a Composite, the chances are about one in ten that you will be right—for the Composite family, which is also named the Daisy or the Sunflower family, contains about an eighth or a tenth of the known species of flowering plants in the world. You can better your chances of being right if you remember a few facts: The flowers of the Composites are tiny, many, and compressed into a flat-topped head, which is surrounded by sepal-like bracts and thus could be taken for a single flower. In this they resemble the Chicory family; indeed, some books put the two families together. The Composites, though, have a watery (not milky) juice; the flower heads live longer, and the rays are lacking in some of the florets. The eight hundred genera of Composites include mostly sun-loving plants, so easy to grow that we think of many of them as weedy, and usually are summer-flowering or fall-flowering. In some organized listings (including this one) the Composites are put last to indicate they are the most highly developed.

Goldenrods

Goldenrods are the all-American flower; few species grow in other countries. One or another of the hundred or more kinds enlivens every part of the United States. Few flowers are more colorful or more cherished. (It is doubtful whether they cause hay fever.) Alabama, Nebraska, and Kentucky have Goldenrod for their state flower; it has often been suggested for our national flower.

The golden-yellow flower heads, composed of ray and tubular flowers, are arranged in five ways:

1. *In flat-topped clusters:*

Grass-leaf Goldenrod: Four feet tall or less; 25-odd florets, about half of them with yellow rays; leaves narrow; late summer; eastern areas; damp places.

Slender Goldenrod: Similar; eighteen inches tall; delicate stem; ribbon-like leaves.

2. *Blossoms in the axils of leaves:*

Blue-stem Goldenrod: Slender, blue-tinged stem, two feet tall; flower heads have several tiny rays and are clustered along the curving stem; common along woody roadsides.

Wide-leaf Goldenrod: Similar, but has broad leaves, zigzag stems, and grows in denser woods.

3. *Plumes with leaves on flowering branches:*

Plume Goldenrod: Earliest (June-November) and one of handsomest; four feet tall; reddish stems; fluffy, large flower masses, curving at the tops; stout, smooth stems that tend to grow in clumps; larger leaves have smaller leaves growing in their axils; dry ground.

Rough-stem Goldenrod: Tall; rough stems; July to October; flower heads have fewer than nine rays; leaves oval, toothed, hairy. Common along roadsides.

4. *Compact plumes:*

Stout Goldenrod: August-October; large flower heads; stout stem; broad throughout; lower leaves up to foot long; smaller upper leaves have wavy edges. (Page 118.)

Downy Goldenrod: Three feet or less.

5. *Common plumes:*

Sharp-leaf Goldenrod: Four feet or less; smooth, angled stem; thin woods; July-September.

Canada Goldenrod: Five feet or less; narrow, willowy leaves, sharply toothed; pyramidal clusters of tiny flowers; July-September; streambanks and fields everywhere.

Showy Goldenrod: To seven feet; trusses of flowers; dry woodlands.

That's just a beginning.

BLAZING STAR

Call them Gayfeathers, Button Snakeroots (because of their button-like tubers and the old belief that they were good for snakebites), or Blazing Star—these are imposing, beautiful plants whose home is primarily the grassy prairies. All are much alike: Erect perennials on whose straight stems are wands of rose, purple, or white flowers in late summer and fall.

Blue Blazing Star, sometimes as tall as six feet, has magenta-purple heads into which are packed thirty or so tube-like florets, each about an inch across and surrounded by bristles. Its leaves are narrow. It prefers dry ground west to Texas.

Prairie Blazing Star has stalks up to four feet. The short, round, purple heads form an attractive spike that sometimes measures eighteen inches. The spikes start blooming at the top. The many leaves are narrow.

Common Gayfeather, often found at the edge of moist woods, has only about a dozen flowers to a head.

Scaly Blazing Star (Rough-spike Gayfeather) has many purple, rayless florets on stalks that grow eighteen inches tall. The fruit has feathery plumes.

Dotted Gayfeather has black spots on leaves and bracts. It lives in dry places from Minnesota to Texas.

Showy Blazing Star has heads that contain only a few flowers, but the heads combine to make long, dense, colorful spikes, which are enhanced by bright lavender bracts.

Northwesterners apply the name Blazing Star to a member of the genus *Mentzelia,* a tall, sturdy, white-stemmed, yellow flower.

Tall Blazing Star has variable, lovely magenta blossoms.

White Snakeroot

Ironweed, of which we have several varieties, has imposing dark purple flower heads at the top (all at about the same height) of six-foot branched, smooth stems. The florets are tubular and without ray petals. Bracts and fruit have bristles. The leaves are narrow, finely toothed, and lance-shaped. It grows in low ground. It belongs to the Composite group.

White Snakeroot (pictured above) is three feet high and white-flowered. The flower-heads are small but numerous. The branches have coarse leaves and point upward.

Boneset grows to four feet and has many tiny grayish flower heads. The stems seem to pierce the leaves.

Joe-Pye Weed grows to eight feet and has dull pink flowers in a big terminal plume. The coarse leaves are in whorls of three or six.

All three like moist thickets in the eastern half of the country and have florets that lack rays. All have fruits tipped with short gray bristles.

Hawkweed has bright red-orange floret rays in heads less than an inch across. Each is on a long, thin, branched, and almost leafless stalk. The low plant spreads by runners all over fields, woods, and roadsides in the north central states. It is weedy or beautiful, as you prefer. Its leaves are rough and hairy and in a rosette at the base. From them rises the foot-high flower stalks. There are a score or two of Hawkweeds, mostly yellow.

THE ASTERS

Aster means star—a good name for these two hundred species that twinkle all over America in late summer and fall. The flower heads have yellow centers (made up of many tubular flowers, which have both pistils and stamens). Surrounding the centers are ray flowers that have only pistils. The form of stem and leaf is one key in identification.

New England Aster: Up to eight feet tall; showy violet-purple flower heads an inch across; thirty or more ray flowers; leaves hairy and clasping the stout hairy branches, untoothed; open places over most of the country.

New York Aster: Slender; smooth; less than three feet high; leaves lance-shaped, slightly toothed, somewhat fleshy; eastern seaboard; about twenty violet-colored rays.

White-wreath Aster (illustrated): Small white heads in large masses; small leaves; many-branched; along roadsides almost everywhere and midwest fields.

Purple Aster: Rough stem; three feet or less; heads an inch across; twenty-five purple rays; leaves heart-shaped and clasping stems; common in dry open places.

Bristly Aster: To eighteen inches tall; stiff stalks branching upward; three-fourths-inch heads at tips of branches; lavender rays; sandy slopes.

Large-leaf Aster: Lilac to white flowers, inch wide, on thick stem that rises from clump of large, heart-shaped, toothed leaves.

Golden Aster: A foot or two tall; large, yellow flowerheads; silky stem; New York southwards.

THE CONEFLOWERS

A native of the Midwest that has moved east and west and one of our most imposing flowers is Black-eyed Susan. Its flower head contains a cone or disk of brown or purplish black tubular flowers, surrounding which are ten or twenty yellow or orange rays. It grows three feet tall or less. The leaves are rather woolly and not toothed; the upper ones are oblong and are attached directly to the stem; the lower leaves are spoon-shaped and have stalks. It blooms from June to September in fields. You might want to know its scientific name, *Rudbeckia hirta;* the second part means pasture; the first part, after the botanist Rudbeck, you see applied to a number of garden plants.

Tall Coneflower is a close relative. Its flower heads are three inches or so across, and have only ten or fewer yellow rays around the green-yellow cone. It grows west to Arizona in damp places. It is tall, many branched, and leafy.

Thin-leaf Coneflower has a dozen orange-yellow ray flowers around a dark purple central disk. The flower heads are only two inches broad, but the branched stems, three to five feet tall, carry scores of flower heads, so the plant is showy indeed. It grows in damp places west to Louisiana.

Others of the forty-odd species of Coneflower are just as eye-filling. Among them are:

Shiny Coneflower: Yellow-orange rays; purple or brown cone; up to three feet tall; dry soil far westward. Showy Coneflower and Two-color Coneflower are similar.

THE SUNFLOWERS

The Sunflowers are tall, rugged plants that have huge, rather flat heads of flowers at the tops of rough stems. The big ones can hardly be confused with any other flower. In some species, the center contains several thousand tiny flowers, around which is a row of bright yellow rays, like petals. The stems turn, so that the largest possible leaf surface is presented to the sun; the flowers turn also. The Sunflower seeds are good food for birds.

Common Sunflower (shown above) sometimes grows as tall as fifteen feet. The flower heads might be six to eight inches broad. It grows in the middle tier of states west to Arkansas. It is the Kansas state flower—a worthy, noble plant.

Prairie Sunflower, practically the same, ranges farther westward.

Wild Sunflower is smaller, two to several feet high. The flower heads are two inches across and have a dozen rays around the center disk. The green structure that supports the head has long bracts. The leaves are three inches long, thin, arranged alternately, and have stalks.

Woodland Sunflower blooms earlier, prefers dry woods, and has leaves that are attached directly to the stem.

Jerusalem Artichoke is at least six feet high, but otherwise like the Wild Sunflower. It grows from edible tubers. The stem is hairy. The lower leaves are about six inches long and very rough. A better name for it is Thin-leaf Sunflower. It likes moist woods.

COMPASSPLANT

The large, deeply cut, toothed leaves of the Compass-plant tend to stand on edge and point north and south—hence the name. It stands ten feet high or more, and is rough, hairy, and resinous. The yellow rays are notched at the tip; the flower heads are three or four inches across. It is found in the Midwest. It blooms in late summer in grasslands. It has several kin, distinguished mostly by the degree to which the leaves are divided into lobes. It is shown above.

Sneezeweed

Common Sneezeweed has a large yellow middle disk, around which are arranged a dozen or so golden yellow rays, three-toothed and drooping. It grows up to six feet tall, from western Massachusetts west to Minnesota and south to Mississippi. It prefers swamps and damp places. (See page 90.)

Swamp Sneezeweed is two to four feet high. Its branches extend upward. Many flower heads grow in leaf axils on tall stems. The fifteen yellow rays are drooping and round-lobed at the tip. The leaves are narrow and somewhat toothed.

Purple Sneezeweed has purple disks. It is common in the Southeast. Orange Sneezeweed (as you would expect) has orange rays.

EMERSON: *Nature pardons no mistakes. Her yea is yea, her nay, nay.*

THISTLE

The plant that probably will survive longer than any other is the Thistle. Spines protect it against cows and children. Hair on the stems keeps away unwanted crawling insects. A strong constitution keeps it going even if a farmer scythes it down. Besides, it has an excellent seed-producing capacity.

Tall Thistle is three to six feet high, maybe more. Lilac-purple heads (two inches across and at the tips of branchlets) contain florets that contain only disk flowers, without rays. The outer bracts are short and prickly. The leaves are usually without lobes, but large and toothed with prickles. It blossoms in late summer in fields and thickets west to Texas and Minnesota.

Wavy-leaf Thistle, depicted above, has purple or pink heads up to three inches wide. White wool covers the leaves and stems. It inhabits fields in the Midwest.

Pasture Thistle is fragrant, one to three feet tall, spiny, and altogether lovely in its bizarre way. Bees and butterflies feast on its nectar, but cattle despise it, hense it makes a bold stand in Northeastern pastures. The flower head is two or three inches across and clear lavender-purple.

Eastern Swamp Thistle (about six feet tall, much branched, and purple flowered) and Western Swamp Thistle grow in wet places.

Western species of different colors include Sierra Thistle (pale yellow or white), Rose Thistle (mauve), and Western Thistle (crimson or reddish).

THE FIRST FAMILIES

Here we list the first families of flowers. It might help you in your adventure of knowing the wildings if you do two things: First, choose from the examples cited below for each family, one with which you are already acquainted or can find close by. Second, fix in your mind the main details that pertain to it and, therefore, to other flowers in its group. So, with these main facts in your head, you will be equipped to go outside and identify scores of flowers—at least by family.

Lily Family (Liliaceæ—lily-*ay*-cee-ee). Regular, showy flowers; perianth has six divisions alike in color and shape. Roots usually are bulbous. Narrow leaves often grow from the base, but sometimes are whorled or in pairs on the stems. Flower parts in threes. Fruit is a capsule. Canada Lily, Trout-Lily, Turkscap Lily, Wood Lily.

Lily-of-the-Valley Family (Convallariaceæ—con-val-larry-*ay*-cee-ee). Main stem underground, sometimes very long. Leaves frequently in rosettes. Flower parts in threes, often small and fragrant. Merrybells, Beadlily, Solomon's Plume, Solomon's Seal.

Iris Family (Iridaceæ—eye-rid-*ay*-cee-ee). Grows from corm, bulb, or rhizome, shallowly buried in ground. Leaves generally are narrow, grasslike, or swordlike, and grow from the base. Colorful flowers in clusters surrounded by bracts. Three sepals look like petals and form the "falls" in Iris; three petals of distinctive form. Iris, Blue Flag, Crested Iris.

Orchis Family (Orchidaceæ—or-kid-*ay*-cee-ee). Irregular but delicate and often showy flowers, often with three petals and three sepals of different colors. One petal makes a lip different from the other petals and, sometimes, a spur at the base. At the base of the lip is a column composed of floral organs fused with the ovary. Fruit is a capsule with many minute seeds. Lady's Slipper, Moccasin Flower, Orchis.

Crowfoot or Buttercup Family (Ranunculaceæ—rah-nun-kew-*lay*-cee-ee). Petals and sepals vary from two or three to fifteen; sometimes petals are absent, and then the sepals look like petals. Alternate leaves, sometimes from the root. Many stamens. Anemone, Buttercup, Hepatica.

Mustard or Cress Family (Cruciferæ—crew-*sif*-fer-ee). Generally small white or yellow flowers; four sepals, four petals, six stamens, of which four are longer than the others. Flowers regular—"cross-shaped" The fruit is a pod. Leaves are alternate. Cress, Rocket.

Pink Family (Caryophyllaceæ—carry-oh-fill-*lay*-cee-ee). Five sepals and petals; stems hairy or downy and sometimes swollen at the joints; leaves narrow and opposite each other on the stem. Catchfly, Silene, Pink.

Rose Family (Rosaceæ—rose-*say*-cee-ee). Usually five regular sepals, five petals, and many stamens. Sepals are borne on a disk. The leaves have stipules, are alternate, and often are many-lobed. Avens, Cinquefoil, Strawberry, Wild Rose.

Pea (Pulse) Family (Leguminosæ—leh-gume-in-*oh*-see). Corolla is bilateral; i. e., it suggests a butterfly. Five irregular petals; the two lower petals are united to form a "keel." Generally ten stamens in a tube. The leaves have stipules and often are compound or rarely simple and alternate. Fruit is a legume. Pea, Sweet Pea, Clover, Indigo, Lupine, Vetch.

Parsley (or Carrot) Family (Umbelliferæ—um-bell-*lif*-fer-ee). Many tiny flowers in umbels—i. e., rising from one point on a stem; five petals and five stamens, often yellow or white. Leaves are alternately arranged and usually compound. The stem generally is hollow. Queen Anne's Lace.

Heath Family (Ericaceæ—airy-*kay*-see-ee). Petals form an urn-shaped corolla. Flowers somewhat bilateral or radial. Many are shrubby. Trailing-Arbutus, Azalea, Wintergreen.

Phlox Family (Polemoniaceæ—polymo-nih-*ay*-cee-ee). Small plants with showy flowers in panicles or cymes; flower parts in fives; generally regular corolla, with petals forming a starry disk. Phlox, Sweet William.

Borage Family (Boraginaceæ—bor-ah-gin-*nay*-cee-ee). Leaves often rough and hairy; flower parts in fives; corolla often irregular, with flower groups in spirals. Petals united into a tube, with spreading blades. The short stamens alternate with the petals. Virginia Bluebell.

Mint Family (Labiatæ—lay-be-*ay*-tee). Square stems; usually opposite leaves that are not lobed. Frequently the flowers have two lips. Two of the four stamens are short. Many have a pleasant scent. Mint, Sage, Bergamot.

Snapdragon or Figwort Family (Scrophulariaceæ—scro-full-lar-ih-*ay*-see-ee). Irregular or bilateral corollas, often two-lipped. Irregular stamens. Petals five or four. Leaves whorled, opposite, or alternate. Butter and Eggs, Penstemon, Turtle Head, Gerardia, Betony.

Composite Family (Compositæ—com-*poh*-sih-tee). Small flowers crowded into a single head which is often surrounded by a margin of bracts or ray flowers; leaves frequently opposite or alternate; sun-loving plants; flower head usually flat; watery juice. Aster, Goldenrod, Sunflower, Ironweed, Gayfeather. Chicory family (Dandelion, Hawkweed, Chicory) has milky juice and alternate leaves and the flowers open briefly.

128

A WILD GARDEN
OF OUR OWN

Christine and I soon came to realize how important and interesting it is to know why a wild flower grows where it does—whether in our pasture or down by the creek or up on Short Hill or along our roadsides.

We paid attention to its liking for heat or cold, wet places or dry, much or little rainfall, sunlight or shade, acid or alkaline soil, few or many hours of daylight, hard or friable soil, clay or sand or humus, fertility or austerity. We noted also the company it keeps—which trees, shrubs, weeds, flowers, and grasses like each other or the same climate and soil.

Before we were very deep in our adventure with wild flowers, we began thinking of a wild flower garden of our own. Even though we had, without effort, four types of habitats (roadsides, uplands, pasture, and stream-side) on our land or close at hand, we thought it would be fun to try out some other flowers and ferns in a shady spot in front of our house and to start some different species on Short Hill with a view to making it a wild flower preserve some day.

Our first attempt was a failure, although it taught us a lesson. For the plot before the house we carried woods soil and humus from the Short Hill woods. From a nurseryman we bought three pink Moccasin Flowers and three yellow Lady's Slippers. From a friend we got some Trailing-Arbutus. All died because (we learned later) the soil was too acid for the yellow flower, too alkaline for the other, too deficient in acidity and mycorrhiza—the fungi with which it associates—for the Trailing-Arbutus. We had not provided the proper environment.

We jotted down some basic points:

Wild flowers generally do not thrive when they are pampered like cultivated plants.

Weeds tend to spring up in disturbed soil.

Newly turned earth attracts mice, rabbits, squirrels, and puppies. Some animals like to feed on newly set plants and bulbs, although they might avoid old ones.

Conservation does not mean just transplanting. It means increasing plants by layering, seeds, roots, and cuttings, or letting them reseed.

Don't expect success by just broadcasting some seed. Some soil preparation is needed: Spading to a depth of six inches or so if the soil is hard and mixing in some humus or compost or peat or manure. In good, friable, humus-rich soil, the minimum is scratching the surface and some covering of the seed.

It is wise to test the soil for acid reaction. A soil testing kit can be bought cheaply and used easily.

To plant a wild flower garden, it is best to start with the easier plants. Among them are: Rue-Anemone, Baneberry, the Bellworts, Bloodroot, Columbine, Hepatica, Herb Robert, Jack-in-the-Pulpit, Larkspur, Saxifrage, Phlox, Wild Geranium, Solomon's Seal, Silene, the Trilliums, Violets, Wild Ginger.

Don't despise a flower because it is common.

Transplanting is best done on a cloudy, misty day. Avoid doing it on a windy day.

If you know some wild flower haunt is to be cleared off, try to rescue the plants.

In making your own wild flower garden, an harmonious, natural grouping is best. Avoid the artificial.

Find out about your state's laws to protect wild flowers.

One can plant seeds of wild flowers any time after they have ripened. Usually, however, they must stay in the ground over winter. Hence it is best to sow the seed in flats or in pots in a mixture of sand, soil, and peatmoss. The container can be left outdoors until late winter and then brought indoors to germinate. They are planted outside when the ground can be worked.

Some wild flowers bloom the first spring, but others will not bloom for two years or more—among them Virginia Bluebells, Bloodroot, Trilliums, Pasqueflower, and Squirrel Corn.

Some wild flowers (the Lupines, among them) do not like to be transplanted. They are best started as seed in the new kind of pots that disintegrate in the ground, so that the roots are not disturbed. Plants with bulbs or fleshy roots are easiest to move—after the foliage has died back in summer and fall.

WHERE WILD FLOWERS GROW
Meadows and Fields

An open meadow like ours is the home of a myriad wild flowers and other intriguing plants.

I daresay this land was covered years ago with Oak, Hickory, Locust, Maples, Elms, Walnut, Sassafras, and Pines, just as much of the East was before it was cleared for homes, farms, roads, and towns, and before people became so careless with fire. When it remains untouched for several years, the trees try to come back again, in a steady progression toward a stable condition, which we call climax vegetation. One step in that relentless march, I suppose, is represented by the pestiferous Sumac, Poison Ivy, and Honeysuckle.

Along our old stone walls a fascinating variety of plants take root: The creamy-flowered Elderberry, whose purple fruit the birds relish; the shrubby Mulberry; Choke-Cherry, Bayberry, briars, and Ferns.

The soil has a good deal of stone and clay in it, although the lower spots, where grass and weeds have flourished and died, the ground is less hard and Bluegrass holds its own. Drainage is good. There is little shade. The soil tends to be acid in reaction.

From those details you get a picture of a country meadow and field, at least enough to transfer the main details of soil, plant associations, and climate to a comparable place that you own or visit. If you learn to observe such items, you will know which wild flowers to look for in any particular environment, which you can plant there, and which to expect to find at certain seasons.

Here, generally speaking, you find the bold flowers of summer, not the shy spring blossoms, which tend to be flowers of the woodlands. In the drier parts of pasture and field, few flowers come before June. Among the first probably will be Star-of-Bethlehem, a member of the Lily family that has starry, six-pointed, white flowers in a flat-topped group, about ten inches tall; Star-Grass, a small bulbous plant with sparse, flat groups of golden flowers; and Blue-eyed-Grass, an Iris whose small, violet-blue blossoms are on wiry, eight-inch stalks above tufts of slender, grass-like leaves.

Then, as summer advances, look for Robin's-Plantain, a lavender-pink Daisy with hairy, foot-tall stalks.

A half dozen members of the Pink family, all natives of Europe, stay until fall: The sprawly, white Chickweed; the familiar rose-pink, hairy Corn-Cockle; crimson, woolly, Mullein-pink; the sticky, hairy, and branchy White Campion; rose-pink Catchfly; the entrancing Deptford Pink, and the pale pink, clustered Bouncing Bet.

You will recognize many old friends: The winsome Butter and Eggs and Blue Toadflax, the white bells of Dogbane, the ever-present lavender-blue Chicory, white-clustered and feathery-leaved Yarrow, Queen Anne's Lace, fragrant and yellow Evening-Primrose, and St. Johnswort.

In July and later you will greet Butterflyweed, rough and orange; Wild Rose and Pasture Rose; Milkweed of several sorts; Black-eyed Susan and her cousin, the Sneeze-weed; and, if you are lucky, Canada Lily and Wood Lily.

As summer merges into autumn, there will be Berga-mot; Meadow Beauty, which is pink, and Meadow Sweet, which has a pyramid of tiny white blossoms; Gerardia; golden, white, and blue Asters, and their bluff cousins, the Thistles. Then come also the prized Goldenrods.

In moist meadows (not ours) there will be others: The Northern Camas, in limy, cool, spots; Narrow-leaf Iris; Bowman-root; Great Solomon's Seals; on ledges and slopes, the Onions, Crinkle-root, Cress, Saxifrage.

You know now why Christine and I cherish our little meadow.

ROADSIDES

In memory or right here and now you see a dry and sandy bank along a road or railroad track. Very likely the memory is a pleasant one; of a country road perhaps, made colorful and pleasant for a man and his boy and his dog and for birds and rabbits and other wildlife by shrubs, wild flowers, and trees. It was lovely the whole year, you remember—in spring, the Violets; in summer, the Butterflyweed; in fall, the Aster and Goldenrod; in winter, the silhouettes of the branches of trees and the berries and the tracks of the furred creatures that found shelter and food among them.

But the actuality might be far different. Very likely the roadside you see before you has naked banks, left bare as the road was straightened and widened and nothing has yet had a chance to grow. There is no life there, whether plant or animal. Wild flowers could grow there again. It is good highway maintenance practice to see that they do; it is good conservation, for birds would come back to wage their battle against insect pests.

But wherever and whatever the road or bank, the plants that grow there are mostly quite different from those that inhabit moist, shady places. The chances are that the wild flowers will be taller than the woods flowers; rougher of stem and leaf; yellow or orange or red in color. These are the sturdier plants with harder competition to keep alive, and therefore more persistent; they are the sun-loving plants, and they tend to bloom in late summer or fall; they are the ones that depend on wind or insects to spread their pollen.

Probably the setting is determined by some bushes—Bayberry or Round-leaved Dogwood or Sumac or some sort of Juniper or Cedar. More probably the bank is grassy. Poison Ivy and wild Honeysuckle may be taking over, killing all that come within their relentless grasp.

Considered in terms of the whole twelve months, the outstanding flowers very likely are the Asters, small lavender or white blooms that sometimes blanket all in a cloud of pale color; the Goldenrod in its blaze of gold; and the higher, rougher, purplish Milkweeds. These are of the autumn, when Nature makes a last, bold gesture before sky and hills turn gray and white.

But before they take the stage, there are (or could be, which might be more important!) an exciting parade: Of Clovers and Vetch and Morning Glories, pink, red, magenta, lavender, white, purple; of Stonecrop, False Indigo, the Blazing Star, Wood Lily, or Day Lily, whose tawny copper has spilled out of old-fashioned gardens. Sweet-clover there is, too. Perhaps you will find Lupines, Lespedeza, and Saxifrage.

Before that, as spring turns into summer, you might have to seek the Violets—Birdfoot and Canadian and one of many others depending on how far west you live from the Atlantic. Of ferns, there might be the Hay-scented. Maybe, if water stands in the ditch, you will find Cat-tails.

Treasures enough, are these, in what we are prone to consider waste places or, in these later days, have let become waste places without much effort on our part to redeem them.

What better project, what more patriotic endeavor could a group of boys and girls and civic-minded citizens have than this?—to beautify the nation's roadsides with native flowering trees, shrubs, and flowers. And to each his own, if it fits: Sunflowers, Goldenrods, Dogwood, and many more.

MILTON: *In those vernal seasons of the year, when the air is calm and pleasant, it were an injury and sullenness against Nature not to go out and see her riches, and partake in her rejoicing with heaven and earth.*

WOODS AND FORESTS

Before the leaves are full on the Oak and Hickory, the Birch and Black Cherry, the Sassafras and Dogwood; before the shade is dense and all the birds have returned; before the sun is high and the heat of the summer is here —then you will see in the woodlands some of our shyest, brightest, and daintiest wild flowers.

They are the ones usually that can store food in thick rootstocks and burst early into flower. They depend more on the crawling insects to carry their pollen. They do not need great height or the brightest colors to insure that wind or flying insects reach them and perform the all-important task of pollination. What they lack in flamboyancy they make up for with fragrance, delicate colors, and a retiring nature, so that you must seek them and have that much more joy in finding them. It is too bad that these are the most vulnerable of the wildings, the ones that are disappearing more rapidly than the others, because their homes are being cleared for other things.

In April you will find the furry Hepaticas; they and others wear coats for protection against the cold and late snows. The Trilliums and Bloodroot will be among the first, also; their protection is the leaf that clasps the budding flower. In more open, sunnier spots you will find the Dutchman's Breeches and Squirrel Corn. In spots where the ground is moist and clayey, you find the Maidenhair Fern, and Baneberries with their red or white flowers. On the northerly slopes, if you are indeed fortunate, there will be Trailing-Arbutus. The deep leafmold and litter of leaves will harbor the Wild-Ginger, which never grows beyond reach of the grubs it depends on.

The Lady's Slipper will be there in rich soil, unless people have been careless or selfish with it. Perhaps, not too far away, a Showy Orchis or Moccasin Flower. Jack-in-the-Pulpit, Wild Geranium, Columbine, and May-Apple, of course, will be there.

The succession will go on for some weeks until the trees have their full canopy of leaves; even then, in the open places, you will find a satisfying parade—of Rue-Anemone, Blue Wood Aster, Bellwort, Solomon's Seal, Loosestrife, Spring Beauty, the Yellow and Common Violets, Oakesia, Saxifrage.

At higher levels you might find some of those; likelier still you will encounter Corydalis, Shinleaf, Pipsissewa, Clintonia and Wintergreen.

And while you enjoy all these and marvel at the care Nature used in making them, remember that, once gone from these woods, they may never come back.

The big, dense woods you enter as you do a cathedral. The trees tower above you, and all is still, except the birds and the brook. The old Hemlocks make a cool shade. The great noble Oaks have dropped their leaves for generations, and have added to the acid humus in the ground. Or the trees might be Birch, Beech, Sweet Gum, Holly, or Tulip Tree.

In this shade you may find rather few shrubs and flowering plants—Blueberry, perhaps, in highly acid ground; Mountain Laurel or Kalmia or Azalea; dwarf Yew and Oregon Grape; and maybe Witch Hazel, depending on your section of the country. The Bunchberry, the shining Club Moss, the Snowberry, and patches of Rattlesnake Plantain could well be there. Look also for Pipsissewa, Pyrola, Twin Flower, and Purple Raspberry. In moist places, before summer, there might be Cucumber Root, Goldenseal, Rosybells, and Twisted-stalk.

Look closely for the Beech Drops, Bellwort, Mayflower, Herb Robert, Sweet White Violet, Pink Moccasin Flower. Where there is no sun, for they need none, will be Indian Pipe, Beechdrops, and Coral-root.

LAKESIDE, PONDSIDE, SEASIDE

The banks of lakes and ponds have a life of their own. Birds, soil, moisture, fish, animals, and vegetation are quite unlike those you find on mountains or prairies or swift streams or shores of a salty sea. For these conditions a different set of plants is adapted. To the plainsman they are apt to be less beautiful than flowers he knows in woods and prairies, but more strange and bizarre.

Trees, if there are any, might be Red Oak, Willow of one species or another, Pin Oak. Shrubby growth might be Alder or Elder or small Willows, their roots reaching for the water.

Pickerel-weed grows in the water near the shore, its flowers a blue cloud in midsummer. Arrow Head sends up its white clusters not far away. Spatterdock, which you might call any one of a score of local names, is a yellow star in the mud, and one of the native Water-Lilies grows where the water is still. Look closely at these plants and see how each is provided with narrow leaves, or pliable stems, or water-shedding leaf surfaces, or variations in size in order to cope with the changing conditions of their watery habitat. Note also the insects that visit them; maybe you will see a pattern or purpose in the colors that are there and those that are missing.

Along the banks, and in moist, shaded ground, grow Tall Day Flower, Fairy Wand, Lizard-tail, Swamp Smart-weed, and American-Lotus, all of them lush and shining, as befits their favored habitat.

Look also for the Arum, Sweet Flag, and Crowfoot. Look also for the Larger Blue Flag, Swamp Saxifrage, Skunk-Cabbage, Water Plantain. Probably some distance away, you will find a precious Closed Gentian. Standing in the water or on a moist bank will be a colony of Cat-tails. Very likely near at hand will be Sedge and one or another of the large Grass family.

At the seaside you will find some of those plants, but also others that like the salt, sand, and acid soil.

Among the Beach Plum, Blueberry, Groundsel, Sand-myrtle, Holly, and Scrub Oak you are apt to find the Beach-pea, Wintergreen, and the dark-leaved mats of Bearberry. Again, the Trailing-Arbutus might be at home there. The plants known locally as Sea Pinks and Marsh Pinks cover the ground with a vivid carpet. Someplace or other will be the New York Aster and a variety of Goldenrod, which we encounter in so many other places— maybe also the Butterflyweed, two or three kinds of Gerardia, Prickly-Pear, Birdfoot Violet, Wild Indigo, Bracken, and Marsh Fern. Seaweed and the Grasses, of course, trying ceaselessly to hold their own.

Truly, there is a wide scope in such a place for naturalist and flower lover.

MARSH AND SWAMP

If there were nothing else on the banks of a brook or in a sunny marsh, these would be more than enough: Virginia Bluebells, Iris, and Cardinal Flower. But there are many more to gladden eye and heart. Here the Cardinal Flower likes it best and makes a fiery show. Here also the Turkscap Lily luxuriates. Farther away in the meadow lives the Fringed Gentian; closer to the place where the brook emerges from the woods is the Closed Gentian, both of regal form and color.

Where the brook makes a broad sweep around the meadow, that is the place where the Virginia Bluebell lives and shines forth pink and then blue, as though the sky itself were there.

Where the stream gets lazy and makes a marsh, you will find the Iris, the flags of blue or many other colors. Before the snow has gone, you will find Skunk-Cabbage, and know that spring is close at hand.

The white, round, glistening flowers of Turtle Head will appear in the high ground. Among the Grass will be Painted Cup, yellow and scarlet; you will not find one without the other.

As the Marsh-Marigold ends its season, you will find Swamp Milkweed, the snowy Boneset, Joe-Pye Weed, and the shiny leaves and pouched, orange flowers of the Jewel-weed. The Meadow Lily, yellow and red on man-high stalks, and the feathery Meadow-Rue will be there later in the summer, in rich meadow. They will be there, that is, if we permit them to be. Like as not you will find the Broad-leaf Cat-tail, Broad-leaf Arrow Head, and four of the Trilliums—the Wet-dog, Nodding, Great, and Painted Trillium.

Blue-eyed Grass, Grass-of-Parnassus, False-Hellebore, Ironweed, Jack-in-the-Pulpit, Canada Lily, Swamp Milkweed, Monkey Flower, the Fringed Orchis, Sneezeweed, Lanceleaf Violet, Wild Senna, Tall Meadow-Rue—those also are plants you will meet in the open, sunny marsh, each in its own season and each in its own place.

A bog is colder, more stagnant, less inviting than a marsh, but even there we find some of our most beautiful plants. Fortunate is the person who has a bog not too far away where he can enjoy the Skunk-Cabbage, Buckbean, Bunchberry, Wild Calla, Golden Club, the insect-catching Pitcher Plant, the Lady's Slippers, Bog Solomon's Plume, Canada Mayflower, Grass Pink, Viscid Triantha, Rose Pogonia, Sundew, Tufted Loosestrife, Water-Hemlock—each in its own good time. The Slender Yellow-eye likes the bog and also the sandy, acid flat; in the sandy margin will be the Upland Yellow-eye.

Such a bog is at the opposite pole from the desert or the mountain valley, from the steaming swamps far south, or the black northern forest. But in each of them some charming wild flower grows, put there for us to see and enjoy.

—And so, go where you will with open eye and receptive mind, you will find new meaning in William Cullen Bryant's lines:

> My heart is awed within me when I think
> Of the great miracle that still goes on,
> In silence round me—the perpetual work
> Of Thy creation, finished, yet renewed
> Forever. Written on Thy works I read
> The lesson of Thy own eternity.

INDEX

Only English names are given here. In some instances, synonyms are listed for the common names used in this book.

Two stars (**) after a name indicate that the flower should not be picked, at least not near large towns or tourist centers. One star indicates that the flower may be picked if the roots are not disturbed and plenty of flowers are left to go to seed. Those not starred may be picked freely. This material is based on a list prepared by the Wild Flower Preservation Society, 3740 Oliver Street, N. W., Washington 15, D. C.

(WG) after the page numbers indicates that the species is suitable for a wild garden if the plant's requirements of soil, acidity, sun, shade, etc., are met.

143

My Wild Flower Diary

Name of Flower	Where I Found It	When	Other Notes

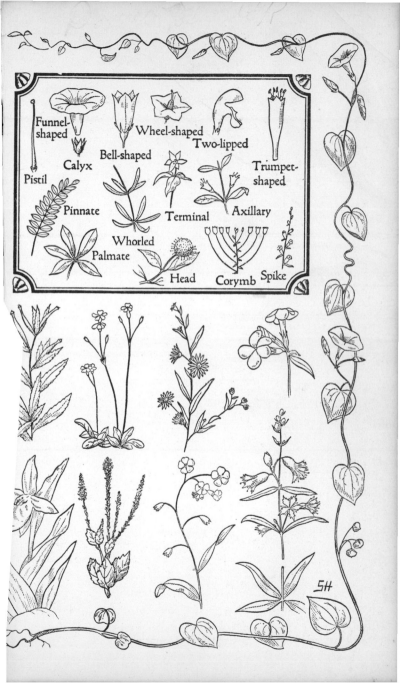

Funnel-shaped

Calyx

Pistil

Wheel-shaped

Two-lipped

Bell-shaped

Trumpet-shaped

Pinnate

Terminal

Axillary

Whorled

Palmate

Head

Corymb

Spike